TABLE OF CONTENTS

How can you multiply 3-digit numbers by 1-digit numbers?

Explore

You can use place value to multiply **2-digit numbers**.

Multiply the ones. Multiply the tens.
The **product** is 420.

How can you multiply **3-digit numbers**?   4 × 132

$$\begin{array}{r} \overset{2}{84} \\ \times\ 5 \\ \hline 420 \end{array}$$ 20 ones
regrouped
as 2 tens

Think

4 × 132 is the same as __4__ groups of __132__.

132 = __1__ hundred, __3__ tens, and __2__ ones.

4 groups
of 132

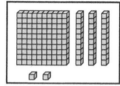 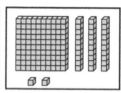 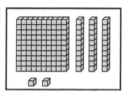 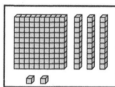

Connect

Set up the problem vertically. Follow the steps to multiply.

Step 1. Multiply the ones.	**Step 2.** Multiply the tens.	**Step 3.** Multiply the hundreds.
$$\begin{array}{r} 13\!2 \\ \times\ 4 \\ \hline 8 \end{array}$$	$$\begin{array}{r} \overset{1}{1}3\!2 \\ \times\ 4 \\ \hline 28 \end{array}$$	$$\begin{array}{r} \overset{1}{1}32 \\ \times\ 4 \\ \hline 528 \end{array}$$
Multiply 2 ones by 4 to get 8 ones.	Multiply 3 tens by 4 to get 12 tens. Regroup 10 tens as 1 hundred.	Multiply 1 hundred by 4 to get 4 hundreds. Add the regrouped hundred.

The product of 4 × 132 = 528.

Let's Talk

If there are only 4 hundreds blocks in the model, why does the product have 5 hundreds?

Instruction

STAMS® series E

S trategies
T o
A chieve
M athematics
S uccess

Curriculum Associates®

ISBN 978-0-7609-6855-0
©2011—Curriculum Associates, LLC
North Billerica, MA 01862
20 19 18 17 16

Fill in the blanks. Solve the problem.

Members of the fifth grade class are giving 3 performances of their spring concert. The school theater has 248 seats. They sold all the tickets available for each show.

How many tickets did they sell in all?

- 3 × 248 is the same as _____ groups of _____.

  248 = _____ hundreds, _____ tens, and _____ ones.

- Follow the steps to multiply 3 × 248.

  1. Multiply the ones.

  So, multiply 8 ones by 3 to get _____ ones.

  Regroup 20 ones as _____ tens.

  2. Multiply the tens.

  So, multiply 4 tens by 3 to get _____ tens.

  Add the regrouped ones to get _____ tens.

  Regroup 10 tens as _____ hundred.

  3. Multiply the hundreds.

  So, multiply 2 hundreds by 3 to get _____ hundreds.

  Add the regrouped hundred to get _____ hundreds.

Solution: The fifth grade class sold _____ tickets.

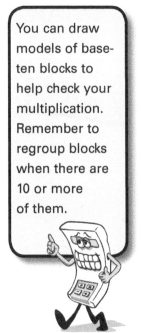

You can draw models of base-ten blocks to help check your multiplication. Remember to regroup blocks when there are 10 or more of them.

$$\begin{array}{r} \square\square \\ 2\ 4\ 8 \\ \times\qquad 3 \\ \hline \square\square\square \end{array}$$

Your Turn ▷ **Now, use what you know to solve this problem.**

1. A store ordered 5 boxes of rulers. There are 125 rulers in each box. What is the total number of rulers the store ordered?

  Ⓐ 505

  Ⓑ 580

  Ⓒ 625

  Ⓓ 705

How can you multiply 3-digit numbers by 2-digit numbers?

Explore

To multiply a 3-digit number by a 1-digit number, use place value to multiply each digit in the 3-digit number by the 1-digit number. Regroup as needed.

$$\begin{array}{r} {}^{1\,1}236 \\ \times\ \ 3 \\ \hline 708 \end{array}$$

How can you multiply 3-digit numbers by 2-digit numbers?   23 × 381

Think

Estimate the product. Round **factors** to numbers that are easy to multiply.

Round 23 to __20__. Round 381 to __400__.

The estimated product is __20__ × __400__ = __8,000__.

The actual product should be close to __8,000__.

Connect

Find the actual product. Set up the problem vertically. Follow the steps.

Step 1. Multiply the ones, tens, and hundreds by the ones.	**Step 2.** Multiply the ones, tens, and hundreds by the tens. Write 0 in the ones place because the tens are being multiplied.	**Step 3.** Add the **partial products** to find the product.

$$\begin{array}{r} {}^{2}381 \\ \times\ \ 23 \\ \hline 1143 \end{array}$$

$$\begin{array}{r} {}^{1}381 \\ \times\ \ 23 \\ \hline 1143 \\ 7620 \end{array}$$

$$\begin{array}{r} 381 \\ \times\ \ 23 \\ \hline 1143 \\ +\ 7620 \\ \hline 8,763 \end{array}$$

Multiply 381 by 3 ones.   Multiply 381 by 2 tens.   Add 1143 and 7620.

The actual product of 23 × 381 = 8,763. This is close to the estimate 8,000.

Let's Talk

Why was it necessary to write a zero in the second partial product?

Fill in the blanks. Solve the problem.

Martino put $186 into his bank account each month for 18 months. How much money did Martino save?

For this product, you need to regroup when multiplying the ones in the 2-digit number, but not the tens. Be sure to **not** add the regrouped numbers again when you find the second partial product.

■ Estimate the product.

　Round 18 to _____. Round 186 to _____.

　The estimated product is _____ × _____ = _____.

　The actual product should be close to _____.

■ Follow the steps to multiply 18 × 186.

　1. Multiply the ones, tens, and hundreds by the ones. So, multiply _____ by _____ ones. Regroup as needed. Write the partial product.

　2. Multiply the ones, tens, and hundreds by the tens. So, multiply 186 by _____ ten. Write _____ in the ones place because the tens are being multiplied. Write the partial product.

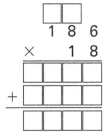

　3. Add the partial products to find the product.

■ The actual product, _____, is close to the estimate of _____. The answer is reasonable.

Solution: Martino saved $_____ in all.

Your Turn ▷ **Now, use what you know to solve this problem.**

　2. There are 365 days in 1 year.
　　How many days are there in 21 years?
　　Show your work.

21 × 365 = _____ days

Solve the problem. Then read why each answer choice is correct or not correct.

Solve

Mr. Wilson drives 143 miles round-trip to work each day.

What is the total number of miles he drives in 9 days?

Ⓐ   967

Ⓑ   1,142

Ⓒ   1,287

Ⓓ   1,627

Check

Check to see if you chose the correct answer.

Find the product of 9 × 143. Set up the problem vertically.

Multiply the ones: 9 × 3 = 27. Regroup 20 ones as 2 tens.

Multiply the tens: 9 × 4 = 36. Add the regrouped tens and regroup 30 tens as 3 hundreds.

Multiply the hundreds: 9 × 1 = 9. Add the regrouped hundreds.

$$\begin{array}{r} {}^{3\,2}143 \\ \times\quad 9 \\ \hline 1{,}287 \end{array}$$

The product is 1,287.

So, the correct answer is Ⓒ.

Why are the other answer choices not correct?

Ⓐ 967	The regrouped amounts are *not* included in this answer.
Ⓑ 1,142	Each digit in 143 was *added* to 9 instead of multiplied by 9.
Ⓓ 1,627	The 2 regrouped tens were *multiplied* instead of added.

- Identify the numbers being multiplied. Write the multiplication vertically with the number with fewer digits on the bottom.
- Regroup amounts as needed. Remember to add (not multiply) the regrouped amounts.
- When multiplying a 3-digit number by the tens place of a 2-digit number, write a zero in the ones place to be sure the partial product has the correct place value.

3. What are the partial products when multiplying 492 × 13?

   Ⓐ 1,476 and 4,920

   Ⓑ 14,760 and 492

   Ⓒ 2,476 and 492

   Ⓓ 1,276 and 4,920

4. There are 124 seats on a small airplane. An airline owns 35 of these airplanes. How many seats are there in all the airplanes?

   Ⓐ 992

   Ⓑ 1,590

   Ⓒ 3,724

   Ⓓ 4,340

5. An animal shelter can hold 268 dogs. Each dog needs 2 bowls: one for its food and one for its water. What is the total number of bowls the animal shelter needs?

   Ⓐ 426

   Ⓑ 490

   Ⓒ 536

   Ⓓ 686

6. A book company is inviting 8 students from each school to submit an essay for a contest. There are 231 schools. What is the total number of students who may submit essays to the contest?

   Ⓐ 2,318

   Ⓑ 1,848

   Ⓒ 1,648

   Ⓓ 1,119

Study the model. It is a good example of a written answer.

Student Model

Show

Each shelf in the public library can hold 267 books. There are 36 shelves in the fiction section. How many fiction books can this section of the library hold?

Use pictures, words, or numbers to show your work.

Estimate. $40 \times 250 = 10,000$

Find 36×267.

1. Multiply 267 by 6 ones.
2. Multiply 267 by 3 tens.
3. Add the partial products.

$$\begin{array}{r} {}^{2\,2} \\ {}^{4\,4} \\ 267 \\ \times\ 36 \\ \hline 1602 \\ +\ 8010 \\ \hline 9{,}612 \end{array}$$

> ☑ The student shows each step.

Solution: The library can place __9,612__ books in the fiction section.

> ☑ The student correctly answers the question asked.

Explain

Explain how you got your answer.

I needed to find the product of a 3-digit number and a

2-digit number, so I first estimated: $40 \times 250 = 10,000$.

Then, I multiplied the ones, tens, and hundreds in 267 by

the 6 ones in 36 and wrote the partial product. Next,

I multiplied the ones, tens, and hundreds in 267 by the

3 tens in 36. Because I was multiplying by tens, I wrote

a zero in the ones place of the partial product. Finally,

I added the partial products, 1,602 and 8,010, to find

the product, 9,612.

> ☑ The student gives important details about how to find the product.

> ☑ The student uses the math words *product*, *3-digit number*, *2-digit number*, *estimate*, and *partial products*.

CHECKLIST

Did you . . .

☐ show each step?

☐ answer the question asked?

☐ give important details?

☐ use math words?

7. A battery can power a radio for 201 hours. For how many hours can a 24-pack of batteries power the radio?

Use pictures, words, or numbers to show your work.

Solution: A 24-pack of batteries can power the radio for _____ hours.

Explain how you got your answer.

_____

_____

_____

_____

_____

_____

As you solve multiplication problems, remember to
- write the steps to multiply 3-digit numbers by 1- or 2-digits.
- add the regrouped amounts.
- add the partial products together to find the product.
- estimate to check if your answer is reasonable.

Solve each problem.

8. A skateboard company produces 258 skateboards each week. Every skateboard has 4 wheels. How many wheels does the company use each week to produce the skateboards?

   Ⓐ 802

   Ⓑ 1,032

   Ⓒ 2,584

   Ⓓ 4,258

9. Brooke is using a hose to fill a swimming pool. The hose adds 326 gallons of water to the pool each hour. How many gallons of water can Brooke add to the swimming pool in 5 hours?

   Ⓐ 1,630 gallons

   Ⓑ 1,510 gallons

   Ⓒ 1,500 gallons

   Ⓓ 911 gallons

10. A movie complex has 12 theaters. Each theater has 328 seats. What is the total number of seats in the movie complex?

   Ⓐ 984

   Ⓑ 1,646

   Ⓒ 3,400

   Ⓓ 3,936

11. A spider has 8 legs. Which is the most reasonable estimate for the total number of legs 532 spiders have?

   Ⓐ 580

   Ⓑ 3,600

   Ⓒ 4,000

   Ⓓ 5,800

12. One truck carries 682 oranges. How many oranges do 12 trucks carry?

   Ⓐ 12,682

   Ⓑ 8,184

   Ⓒ 6,700

   Ⓓ 2,046

13. A farmer bought 362 packages of seeds. Each package contains 24 seeds. How many seeds did the farmer buy in all?

Ⓐ 2,172

Ⓑ 2,534

Ⓒ 3,860

Ⓓ 8,688

14. One chocolate-chip cookie has 138 calories. Write an equation that shows the total number of calories in 9 chocolate-chip cookies.

_____

15. A zookeeper feeds the giraffes 382 pounds of food each week. How many pounds of food does the zookeeper need to feed the giraffes for one year?
(Hint: There are about 52 weeks in one year.)

Use pictures, words, or numbers to show your work.

Solution: The zookeeper needs _____ pounds of food.

Explain how you found your answer.

_____

_____

_____

_____

_____

Lesson 2 DIVIDE MENTALLY

 How can you use basic facts and place value to divide multiples of 10 and 100?

Explore

Division means separating a whole into equal groups.

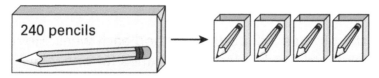

If 240 pencils are divided into 4 equal groups, how many pencils will be in each group?

Think

There are ___240___ pencils in all, and they will be separated into __4__ groups.

So the division problem is ___240 ÷ 4___.

The **dividend** ___240___ is a **multiple of 10**. Some number was multiplied by 10 to get 240.

240 = __24__ tens

4 = __4__ ones

Connect

Think of a **basic fact** related to the problem: 24 ÷ 4 = 6

Then use **place value** to help you divide 240 by 4.

24 tens ÷ 4 = 6 tens, and 6 tens = 60.

There will be 60 pencils in each group.

Let's Talk

What kind of basic fact can you use to check that the example is correct? Choose a basic fact and use it to show that the answer is correct.

Fill in the blanks. Solve the problem.

Marisol wants to put 80 pictures into her photo album. She can fit 4 pictures on each page.

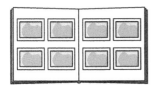

How many pages will Marisol fill in her album?

■ There are _____ pictures. They will be separated into _____ groups.

So the division problem is _____.

■ The dividend _____ is a _____ of 10.

80 = _____ tens

4 = _____ ones

■ Think of a basic fact related to the problem: _____

■ Then use place value to divide 80 by 4:

8 tens ÷ 4 = _____ tens

_____ tens = _____

Solution: Marisol will fill _____ pages in her album.

> Multiples of 10 have a zero in the ones place.

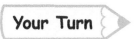 **Your Turn**   **Now, use what you know to solve this problem.**

1. Andrew's soccer club has 180 players. They are separated into 9 teams. Each team has the same number of players. Which basic fact can help you find how many players are on each team?

Ⓐ 18 − 9 = 9

Ⓑ 9 + 9 = 18

Ⓒ 18 ÷ 9 = 2

Ⓓ 9 × 9 = 81

 **How can you mentally divide by multiples of 10?**

Explore

You can use basic facts and place value to help you divide.

On Saturday, 560 people visited a new display at the museum. Only groups of 70 people were allowed to see the display at one time. How many groups of people saw the display at the museum?

Think

There are __560__ people in all, and there were __70__ people in each group.

The division problem is __560 ÷ 70__.

The dividend __560__ and the **divisor** __70__ are __multiples__ of 10.

560 = __56__ tens

70 = __7__ tens

Think of a related basic fact: __56 ÷ 7 = 8__

Connect

Use place value to help you divide 560 ÷ 70:

56 tens ÷ 7 tens = 8 ones

8 ones = 8

Eight groups of people saw the display at the museum.

Another way to find the answer is to write a simpler problem. Cross out the *same* number of zeros in the dividend and the divisor. Then divide.

560 ÷ 70 → 56 ÷ 7 = 8

Crossing out 1 zero is the same as dividing by 10.
560 ÷ 10 = 56 and 70 ÷ 10 = 7.

If you divide the dividend and divisor by the same number, it does not change the quotient.

Let's Talk

Why can mental math be used to divide multiples of 10 and 100?

Fill in the blanks. Solve the problem.

Mrs. Ramirez spent $1,600 on new furniture. She is going to pay the same amount each month for 20 months.

How much will Mrs. Ramirez pay each month?

■ Mrs. Ramirez will pay $ _____ in all.

   She will pay the same amount for _____ months.

   So the division problem is _____.

■ The dividend _____ is a _____ of 100.

   The divisor _____ is a _____ of 10.

   1,600 = _____ hundreds

   20 = _____ tens

■ Use a basic fact and place value to help you find the answer:

   _____ ÷ _____ = _____

   _____ hundreds ÷ _____ tens = _____ tens

   8 tens = _____

Solution: Mrs. Ramirez pays $ _____ each month.

> Since 100 is a multiple of 10, any **multiple of 100** is also a multiple of 10.

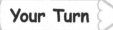 **Your Turn**   **Now, use what you know to solve this problem.**

2. A scientist has 420 grams of a gray powder. She will separate the powder into 6 equal samples. How many grams will each sample have? Show your work.

   _____ ÷ _____ = _____ grams

Solve the problem. Then read why each answer choice is correct or not correct.

Solve

A school ordered 180 new desks. They are going to put the same number of desks in each of 9 classrooms.

How many desks will the school put in each classroom?

Ⓐ   9

Ⓑ   20

Ⓒ   27

Ⓓ   90

Connect

Check to see if you chose the correct answer.

There are 180 desks in all.

They will be separated into 9 groups.

The division problem is $180 \div 9$.

$180 = 18$ tens

18 tens $\div 9 = 2$ tens

2 tens $= 20$

So, the correct answer is Ⓑ.

Why are the other answer choices not correct?

Ⓐ 9	The number of tens should be divided by the number of groups. This answer is found by using subtraction.
Ⓒ 27	The number of tens should *not* be added to the number of ones. Division should be used.
Ⓓ 90	This answer is based on the basic fact $18 \div 2$. The basic fact $18 \div 9$ should be used.

Solve each problem. Use the hints to avoid mistakes.

- Identify the dividend and the divisor in each problem.
- Use basic facts and place value to help you divide.
- When you can, cross out zeros in the dividend and divisor to write a simpler problem.

3. A manager of a bookstore ordered 320 books. He is going to place the same number of books on each shelf. He has 4 shelves.

Which number sentence can be used to find the number of books on each shelf?

Ⓐ 32 tens ÷ 4 tens =

Ⓑ 4 tens ÷ 32 =

Ⓒ 320 tens ÷ 4 =

Ⓓ 32 tens ÷ 4 =

4. A train travels 280 miles in 4 hours. It travels the same number of miles each hour. How many miles does the train travel each hour?

Ⓐ 24 miles

Ⓑ 40 miles

Ⓒ 70 miles

Ⓓ 140 miles

5. Hector saved $720. He put the same amount of money in his savings account each month for 8 months. Which number sentence shows how to find the amount he saved each month?

Ⓐ 720 ÷ 8 = 90

Ⓑ 720 ÷ 10 = 72

Ⓒ 720 − 8 = 712

Ⓓ 72 ÷ 8 = 9

6. A wire is 1,200 centimeters long. Imani is going to cut it into 60 equal pieces. What is the length of each piece of wire?

Ⓐ 2 cm

Ⓑ 3 cm

Ⓒ 20 cm

Ⓓ 30 cm

Study the model. It is a good example of a written answer.

Student Model

Show

A movie theater has 480 seats. The seats are arranged into rows of 80 seats. How many rows are in the theater?

Use pictures, words, or numbers to show your work.

There are 480 seats in all, and 80 in each row.

The division problem is $480 \div 80$.

$480 = 48$ tens

$80 = 8$ tens

Think of a basic fact: $48 \div 8 = 6$

Then divide.

48 tens $\div 8$ tens $= 6$ ones

6 ones $= 6$

Solution: ___6___ rows

> ☑ The student shows each step.

> ☑ The student correctly answers the question asked.

Explain

Explain how you got your answer.

I knew from the question that I had to divide 480 by 80.

I needed to find out how many equal groups of 80 can go

into 480. I rewrote 480 as 48 tens and 80 as 8 tens.

Then I used these numbers to find a basic fact that I know:

$48 \div 8 = 6$. That means that $480 \div 80 = 6$, so there

are 6 rows in the theater.

> ☑ The student gives important details about how to use basic facts to divide.

> ☑ The student uses the math words *divide, equal groups,* and *basic fact.*

Your Turn Solve the problem. Use what you learned from the model.

CHECKLIST

Did you . . .

☐ show each step?

☐ answer the question asked?

☐ give important details?

☐ use math words?

7. A store orders 2,400 erasers. The erasers arrive in 20 boxes. Each box contains the same number of erasers. How many erasers are in each box?

Use pictures, words, or numbers to show your work.

Solution: _____ erasers

Explain how you got your answer.

_____

_____

_____

_____

_____

As you solve division problems, you may want to

- use basic facts.
- write simpler problems.
- use multiplication to check your work.

Solve each problem.

8. A factory needs to make 3,200 light bulbs. The factory can make 400 light bulbs each day. Which number sentence shows how many days the factory must work to make 3,200 light bulbs?

   Ⓐ $3,200 - 400 = 2,800$

   Ⓑ $320 \div 4 = 80$

   Ⓒ $3,200 \div 400 = 8$

   Ⓓ $3,200 \div 400 = 80$

9. Mr. Shea brought 300 sheets of paper to art class. He divided them evenly among his 5 students. How many sheets of paper did each student get?

   Ⓐ 6

   Ⓑ 25

   Ⓒ 35

   Ⓓ 60

10. Gianna bought 400 hamburger buns for the school picnic. There are 8 hamburger buns in each package. How many packages did Gianna buy?

    Ⓐ 32

    Ⓑ 48

    Ⓒ 50

    Ⓓ 80

11. The after school reading club has 50 members. Sponsors of the club are giving away 1,500 books. Each member will receive the same number of books. Which number sentence can be used to find how many books each member will receive?

    Ⓐ $150 \div 5 = $ ▨

    Ⓑ $1,500 \div 5 = $ ▨

    Ⓒ $1,500 \times 5 = $ ▨

    Ⓓ $1,500 \times 50 = $ ▨

12. There are 270 students going on a class trip. Each bus can fit 30 students. How many buses are needed to take the students on the trip?

Ⓐ 3

Ⓑ 6

Ⓒ 9

Ⓓ 18

13. A store donated 360 bags of dog food to local animal shelters. Each animal shelter will get 40 bags of dog food. How many animal shelters will get dog food?

Ⓐ 6

Ⓑ 9

Ⓒ 32

Ⓓ 40

14. Mrs. Lopez bought 140 tickets to the fair. She divided the tickets evenly among her 4 children and their 3 friends.

Write a basic fact that can help you find the number of tickets each child got. Then use the fact to find the answer.

Basic fact:

_____

Solution:

_____

_____

15. The fifth grade is presenting a show on three nights. The students sold the same number of tickets for each show. They sold a total of 180 tickets. How many tickets did they sell for each show?

Use pictures, words, or numbers to show your work.

Solution: _____ tickets

Explain how you found your answer.

_____

_____

_____

PART ONE: Learn About Estimating Quotients

 **How can you use compatible numbers to estimate quotients?**

Explore

Some division problems ask you to find an exact answer. Others ask you to find an **estimate**, or an answer that is close to the actual **quotient**.

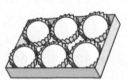

A baker made 658 chocolate candies.
He puts 6 candies into each box.
About how many boxes can he fill?

How can you estimate a quotient when the numbers aren't easy to divide mentally?

Think

Estimate: __658__ ÷ __6__

Use **compatible numbers** to find an estimated quotient.
Find numbers close to the actual numbers that are easy to divide evenly.

Think of a **basic fact** related to the problem.
Focus on the first two digits of the dividend 658: __66__ ÷ 6 = __11__
What number close to 658 can be easily divided by 6? __660__

Connect

Replace the actual numbers with the compatible numbers.

Find the estimated quotient.

658 ÷ 6
↓   ↓
660 ÷ 6 = 110

The baker can fill about 110 boxes.

Let's Talk

How can you determine if the estimate is higher or lower than the exact answer? Use your method to find out.

Fill in the blanks. Solve the problem.

Giuseppe is answering 261 problems for a math-a-thon. The problems fill up 9 pages. Each page has the same number of problems.

About how many math problems are on each page?

- ■ Estimate: _____ ÷ _____

- ■ Think of a basic fact that can help you find compatible numbers.

  _____ ÷ 9 = _____

  What number close to 261 can be easily divided by 9? _____

- ■ Replace the actual numbers with the compatible numbers. Then divide.

  _____ ÷ 9 = _____

Solution: Each page has about _____ math problems on it.

> The word *about* is often a clue for an estimate. *Approximately*, *around*, and *roughly* are other words related to estimates.

Your Turn ▷ **Now, use what you know to solve this problem.**

1. Elijah collected 372 postage stamps. He divided them equally among 4 albums. Which number sentence can he use to estimate the number of stamps in each album?

   Ⓐ 400 − 360 = 40

   Ⓑ 360 ÷ 4 = 90

   Ⓒ 38 ÷ 2 = 19

   Ⓓ 400 ÷ 40 = 10

 How can you use compatible numbers to estimate quotients with 2-digit divisors?

 Explore

You can use division to find the number of **equal groups**, or the number in each group.

How can you estimate quotients with two-digit divisors?

 Think

There are 433 children in summer camp. There are 47 children in each group. About how many groups are there?

Estimate: ___433___ ÷ ___47___

To find compatible numbers for 433 and 47, think of tens and **multiples** of 10.

433 is a little less than ___45___ tens, or 450.

433 is close to ___450___.

47 is almost ___5___ tens, or 50.

47 is close to ___50___.

Connect

Divide using compatible numbers.

450 ÷ 50 = 9

There are about 9 groups of children.

 **Let's Talk**

When can you use estimation to solve a word problem?

Fill in the blanks. Solve the problem.

A farmer planted 588 seedlings for tomato plants. The seedlings are sold in packages of 32.

About how many packages of seedlings did the farmer buy?

- Estimate: _____ ÷ _____

- Find compatible numbers for 588 and 32.

  588 is a little less than _____ tens, or _____.

  32 is a little more than _____ tens, or _____.

- Divide using compatible numbers.

  _____ ÷ _____ = _____

Solution: The farmer bought about _____ packages of seedlings.

> If both numbers are multiples of 10, you can cross out zeros to solve the division problem.
>
> 600 ÷ 30 →
> 60 ÷ 3

Your Turn **Now, use what you know to solve this problem.**

2. Macey has 327 beads. She uses 38 beads to make a necklace. Write a division sentence using compatible numbers to find the approximate number of necklaces Macey can make.

   _____ ÷ _____ = _____

   Macey can make about _____ necklaces.

Solve the problem. Then read why each answer choice is correct or not correct.

Solve

A printer makes 624 newspapers on Sunday. The newspapers are wrapped in stacks of 22.

Which number sentence shows about how many stacks of newspapers the printer makes?

Ⓐ $700 \div 10 = 70$

Ⓑ $60 - 24 = 36$

Ⓒ $66 \div 22 = 3$

Ⓓ $600 \div 20 = 30$

Check

Check to see if you chose the correct answer.

Estimate: $624 \div 22$.

Find compatible numbers for 624 and 22.

There are a little more than 600 newspapers.

There are a little more than 20 newspapers in each stack.

Divide. $600 \div 20 = 30$

So, the correct answer is Ⓓ.

Why are the other answer choices not correct?

Ⓐ $700 \div 10 = 70$	The compatible numbers should be closer to the actual numbers.
Ⓑ $60 - 24 = 28$	The number sentence should use division, not subtraction.
Ⓒ $66 \div 22 = 3$	The dividend and divisor should be rounded to multiples of 10 to rewrite the division sentence.

Solve each problem. Use the hints to avoid mistakes.

- Identify the dividend and divisor from the estimation problem.
- Rewrite the problem using compatible numbers.
- Divide using compatible numbers.

3. A train has enough seats for 312 passengers. The seats are divided evenly among 6 train cars. About how many seats are on each train car?

Ⓐ 30

Ⓑ 40

Ⓒ 50

Ⓓ 60

4. The school auditorium has 468 seats. There are 18 rows of seats. Which is the best estimate for the number of seats in each row?

Ⓐ 20

Ⓑ 23

Ⓒ 28

Ⓓ 50

5. Mrs. Grifo is packing up 144 textbooks. She puts the same number of books in each box. She fills 19 boxes. Which number sentence shows the approximate number of books in each box?

Ⓐ $140 \div 20 = 7$

Ⓑ $140 - 20 = 120$

Ⓒ $100 \div 10 = 10$

Ⓓ $150 \div 10 = 15$

6. A company makes tires for toy cars. Each car gets 4 tires. If the company makes 844 tires, which is a reasonable estimate for the number of cars they can make?

Ⓐ 11

Ⓑ 21

Ⓒ 80

Ⓓ 210

Study the model. It is a good example of a written answer.

Student Model

Show

Amelia's family had a big party. They invited 208 people and set up 34 tables. They put the same number of chairs at each table. Approximately how many people could sit at each table?

Use pictures, words, or numbers to show your work.

Estimate. 208 ÷ 34
Think of a basic fact. 21 ÷ 3 = 7
Find compatible numbers.
208 is a little less than 21 tens, or 210.
34 is a little more than 3 tens, or 30.
Divide using compatible numbers.
210 ÷ 30 = 7

Solution: About __7__ people can sit at each table.

☑ The student shows each step.

☑ The student correctly answers the question asked.

Explain

Explain how you got your answer.

There are 208 people and 34 tables. I needed to

estimate the quotient of 208 ÷ 34. I rounded each

number to a multiple of 10 so that I got compatible

numbers that were easy to divide mentally. I rewrote

the problem as 210 ÷ 30 and got a quotient of 7.

I estimated that 7 people could sit at each table.

☑ The student gives important details about how to find the estimate.

☑ The student uses the math words *estimate*, *multiple of 10*, and *compatible numbers*.

7. The fifth grade raised $546 for a class trip by selling raffle tickets. Each ticket cost $6. Approximately how many raffle tickets did they sell?

Use pictures, words, or numbers to show your work.

> **CHECKLIST**
>
> Did you . . .
>
> ☐ show each step?
>
> ☐ answer the question asked?
>
> ☐ give important details?
>
> ☐ use math words?

Solution: They sold about _____ raffle tickets.

Explain how you got your answer.

_____

_____

_____

_____

_____

As you solve problems in which you estimate quotients, remember to

- think of basic facts that can help you find compatible numbers.
- divide using compatible numbers.

Solve each problem.

8. A florist has 232 flowers. He is going to divide the flowers into 29 vases. Which number sentence can you use to estimate the number of flowers in each vase?

Ⓐ $27 \div 9 = 3$

Ⓑ $240 \div 30 = 8$

Ⓒ $200 \div 20 = 10$

Ⓓ $20 \div 20 = 1$

9. Akiko used these compatible numbers to estimate a quotient.

$$550 \div 50 = 11$$

Which division problem might she have been trying to estimate?

Ⓐ $449 \div 5$

Ⓑ $446 \div 52$

Ⓒ $554 \div 48$

Ⓓ $45 \div 15$

10. This year 336 children auditioned for the talent show in 8 equal sessions. About how many children auditioned at each session?

Ⓐ 10

Ⓑ 20

Ⓒ 30

Ⓓ 40

11. Eduardo's family took a car trip. They traveled 912 miles in 3 days. If they traveled roughly the same number of miles each day, about how many miles did they travel each day?

Ⓐ 300 miles

Ⓑ 250 miles

Ⓒ 200 miles

Ⓓ 150 miles

12. A store has 446 video games. The video games are divided among 7 shelves. Approximately how many video games are on each shelf?

Ⓐ 40

Ⓑ 60

Ⓒ 80

Ⓓ 100

13. Aimee and her mother made 267 cookies for a bake sale. About how many cookies can they put in each of 52 bags?

Ⓐ 5

Ⓑ 10

Ⓒ 15

Ⓓ 20

14. Pedro has 329 baseball cards. He keeps them in packs of 40. About how many packs of cards does Pedro have?

Write a basic fact that can help you find compatible numbers. Then write a division sentence using compatible numbers to find the estimate.

Basic fact:

_____

Division sentence:

_____

Solution:

Pedro has about _____ packs of cards.

15. Vanessa read 182 pages in her book in 1 hour. Approximately how many pages did she read each minute? (Hint: There are 60 minutes in one hour.)

Use pictures, words, or numbers to show your work.

Solution: She read about _____ pages each minute.

Explain how you found your answer.

_____

_____

_____

_____

 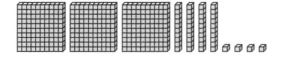 How can you use models to divide by a 1-digit number?

Explore

Division is used to separate a whole into equal groups. Malik used base-ten blocks to show 344.

If he divides the blocks into 3 equal groups, how much will be in each group?

Think

Malik used __3__ hundreds, __4__ tens, and __4__ ones to show 344.

Divide the blocks into __3__ equal groups.

Find how many __hundreds__, __tens__, and __ones__ are in each group.

Connect

Separate the blocks into 3 equal groups.

Regroup the leftover ten as 10 ones. Now there are 14 ones.

Separate the 14 ones blocks into 3 equal groups.

Look at each group. There are 114 in each group, with 2 left over. The **quotient** is 114, with a remainder of 2. The **remainder** tells what is left over.

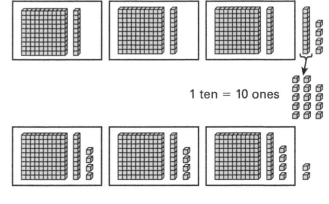

1 ten = 10 ones

Let's Talk

Why did you need to regroup a ten as 10 ones?
Why didn't you have to regroup a hundred?

Fill in the blanks. Solve the problem.

Akiko is dividing 527 into
4 equal groups.

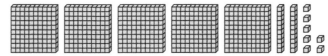

How many are in each group?

■ What blocks did Akiko use to model 527?

_____ hundreds, _____ tens, and _____ ones

■ Draw a model to divide the hundreds into _____ equal groups.

■ There is _____ hundred left over. Regroup the leftover hundred as _____ tens.

■ There are _____ tens in all. Draw to divide the tens and ones into equal groups.

Solution: 527 divided into 4 equal groups is _____, with a
remainder of _____.

> You can write the remainder with a capital R. So, 50 in each group with 2 left over can be written 50 R 2.

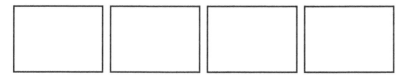 **Your Turn** Now, use what you know to solve this problem.

1. Use these blocks to help you divide 137 into 3 equal groups. How much is in each group? Draw a model.

Ⓐ 46 R 0

Ⓑ 45 R 2

Ⓒ 45 R 0

Ⓓ 42 R 1

How can you divide without using models?

Explore

You've seen how to use models, like base-ten blocks, to find a quotient and remainder.

How can you find a quotient and remainder without using models?

974 ÷ 3

Divide 129 ÷ 2.

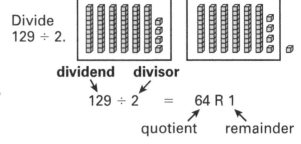

dividend   divisor

129 ÷ 2 = 64 R 1

quotient   remainder

Think

The problem 974 ÷ 3 means divide __974__ into __3__ equal groups. Find how many __hundreds__, __tens__, and __ones__ are in each group. 974 has __9__ hundreds, __7__ tens, and __4__ ones.

Connect

The problem 974 ÷ 3 is also written as 3)974. Follow these steps to find 3)974 using **long division**.

1. *Divide* 9 hundreds into 3 equal groups. Each group has 3 hundreds. Write 3 in the hundreds place. $\begin{array}{r} 3 \\ 3\overline{)974} \end{array}$	**2.** *Multiply* 3 hundreds by the divisor, 3. Write 900 and *subtract*. $\begin{array}{r} 3 \\ 3\overline{)974} \\ -900 \\ \hline 74 \end{array}$
3. *Divide* 7 tens into 3 equal groups. Each group has 2 tens. Write 2 in the tens place. *Multiply* 2 tens by the divisor, 3. Write 60 and *subtract*. $\begin{array}{r} 32 \\ 3\overline{)974} \\ -900 \\ \hline 74 \\ -60 \\ \hline 14 \end{array}$	**4.** *Divide* 14 ones into 3 equal groups. Each group has 4 ones. Write 4 in the ones place. *Multiply* 4 ones by the divisor, 3. Write 12 and *subtract*. $\begin{array}{r} 324 \\ 3\overline{)974} \\ -900 \\ \hline 74 \\ -60 \\ \hline 14 \\ -12 \\ \hline 2 \end{array}$

The quotient is 324, with a remainder of 2. Write 974 ÷ 3 = 324 R 2.

Let's Talk

Which quotient is greater: 974 ÷ 3 or 974 ÷ 5? Why?

Fill in the blanks. Solve the problem.

Cameron needs to divide 500 sheets of paper into 4 groups for math class. How many pieces of paper should he put in each group?

- Divide _____ into _____ equal groups.

  500 has _____ hundreds, _____ tens, and _____ ones.

- Write the problem. ☐)☐

- Divide.

  Divide 5 hundreds into _____ groups. ⟶

  Write _____ in the quotient.

  Divide 10 tens into _____ groups. ⟶

  Write _____ in the quotient.

  Divide 20 ones into _____ groups. ⟶

  Write _____ in the quotient.

```
          ☐
      ☐ )☐
      – ☐
       ————
        100
      – ☐
       ————
         20
      – ☐
       ————
          0
```

You can use multiplication to check division. Multiply the quotient by the divisor, and then add the remainder. The result should equal the dividend.

- The quotient is _____ with _____ remainder.

Solution: Cameron should put _____ pieces of paper in each group.

Your Turn ▷ **Now, use what you know to solve this problem.**

2. There are 6 floats in the spring parade. Juanita wants to divide 728 flowers equally among the floats. How many flowers are given to each float?

   Show your work.

   There are _____ flowers for each float,

   with _____ flowers left over.

Solve the problem. Then read why each answer choice is correct or not correct.

Solve

A batch of 538 pencils came off an assembly line at a factory. They will be packaged in groups of 6 pencils each.

How many packages can be made from these pencils? How many pencils will be left over?

Ⓐ   91 packages, 2 left over

Ⓑ   89 packages, 4 left over

Ⓒ   89 packages, 0 left over

Ⓓ   86 packages, 2 left over

Check

Check to see if you chose the correct answer.

To find the number of packages and pencils left over, you need to divide 538 by 6. Write $6\overline{)538}$.

There are not enough hundreds to divide by 6. Think of 5 hundreds as 50 tens.

Divide 53 tens into 6 groups. ⟶

There are 58 ones.
Divide 58 ones into 6 groups. ⟶

There are 4 ones left. ⟶

$$\begin{array}{r} 89 \\ 6\overline{)538} \\ -480 \\ \hline 58 \\ -54 \\ \hline 4 \end{array}$$

So, the correct answer is Ⓑ.

Why are the other answer choices not correct?

Ⓐ 91 packages, 2 left over	6 should be divided into 53 tens, not 54 tens.
Ⓒ 89 packages, 0 left over	There is a remainder of 4, not 0.
Ⓓ 86 packages, 2 left over	8 tens × 6 = 48 tens, not 50 tens.

- Regroup as needed.
- Carefully write each number of the quotient over the correct place value.
- Check for a remainder.
- Use multiplication to check division.

3. Grace modeled 415 using base-ten blocks as shown.

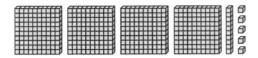

She divided the blocks into 3 equal groups. What are the quotient and remainder?

Ⓐ 196 R 2

Ⓑ 138 R 1

Ⓒ 138 R 0

Ⓓ 105 R 0

4. Which correctly shows a way to write 538 divided by 7?

Ⓐ 538)7

Ⓑ 7) 538

Ⓒ)538 with 7 on top

Ⓓ 7)538

5. Diego is separating 638 baseballs that need to be shared equally among 5 teams. How many baseballs will each team get? How many are left over?

Ⓐ 135 baseballs, 3 left over

Ⓑ 127 baseballs, 8 left over

Ⓒ 127 baseballs, 3 left over

Ⓓ 122 baseballs, 8 left over

6. Which division problem is shown by the model of a quotient and remainder?

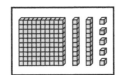 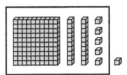

Ⓐ 2)251

Ⓑ 2)125

Ⓒ 2)250

Ⓓ 251)2

Study the model. It is a good example of a written answer.

Student Model

Show

Adam is given 5)613 to solve.
What are the quotient and remainder?

Use a model and long division to show your work.

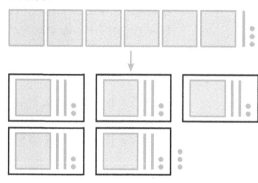

Model

Long Division

```
    122
5)613
 − 500
   113
 − 100
    13
  − 10
     3
```

Solution: ___122 R 3___

Explain

Explain how you got your answer.

First, I drew a model of the dividend using base-ten

blocks. The divisor is 5, so I separated the blocks into

5 equal groups. I divided the hundreds, and then regrouped

the leftover hundred as 10 tens. Next, I divided the tens

and regrouped the leftover ten as 10 ones. I divided the

ones and had a remainder of 3. I also used long division,

which keeps the quotient lined up in the correct place

values. I got the same answer using both ways of dividing.

☑ The student shows each step.

☑ The student correctly answers the question asked.

☑ The student gives important details about how to find the quotient and remainder.

☑ The student uses the math words *dividend, divisor, regroup, remainder,* and *long division.*

CHECKLIST

Did you . . .

☐ show each step?

☐ answer the question asked?

☐ give important details?

☐ use math words?

7. Krystle needs to divide 478 seeds equally among 4 biology classes. How many seeds will each class get? How many seeds are left over?

Use a model and long division to show your work.

Solution: _____

Explain how you got your answer.

_____

_____

_____

_____

_____

As you solve division problems, remember to

- draw pictures to show equal groups.
- carefully regroup numbers as needed.
- pay close attention to the place value of each digit in the quotient.
- use multiplication to check your answer.

Solve each problem.

8. What division problem is shown by the model of a quotient and remainder?

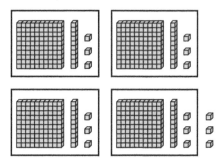

Ⓐ $4\overline{)452}$

Ⓑ $455\overline{)4}$

Ⓒ $4\overline{)455}$

Ⓓ $3\overline{)455}$

9. Maria is dividing 266 pictures onto pages to be put in a photo album. Each page can hold 4 pictures. How many pages does she need for all the pictures?

Ⓐ 61

Ⓑ 64

Ⓒ 66

Ⓓ 67

10. Keisha is separating 656 cereal boxes equally into crates for 5 different charities. How many cereal boxes are in each crate? How many are left over?

Ⓐ 131 boxes, 1 left over

Ⓑ 131 boxes, 0 left over

Ⓒ 130 boxes, 6 left over

Ⓓ 111 boxes, 1 left over

11. Noah used long division to find the quotient and remainder for 742 divided by 6. What is the remainder?

Ⓐ 0

Ⓑ 2

Ⓒ 4

Ⓓ 22

12. Lauren uses base-ten blocks to show dividing 478 into 3 equal groups. How many tens blocks should be in each group?

Ⓐ 7

Ⓑ 5

Ⓒ 3

Ⓓ 1

13. Chang is separating 261 toy cars into 7 bins. Each bin will have the same number of toy cars. How many cars will go into each bin? How many will be left over?

Ⓐ 37 cars, 0 left over

Ⓑ 37 cars, 1 left over

Ⓒ 37 cars, 2 left over

Ⓓ 39 cars, 0 left over

14. An employee at a pet store needs to divide 494 fish equally among 8 large fish tanks. Any leftover fish will be put in a smaller tank on display.

Write the division problem and divide.

How many fish are in the smaller tank?

_____

15. A landscaper divides 482 flowers in 9 equal groups. How many flowers are in each group? How many are left over?

Use pictures, words, or numbers to show your work.

Solution: _____

Explain how you found your answer.

_____

_____

_____

_____

_____

 **How can you model division with zero in the quotient?**

Explore

To **divide** means to separate a whole into equal groups.

You can use models to divide by separating base-ten blocks into equal groups.

What does it mean when there are no tens blocks in the equal groups?

How would you model $323 \div 3$?

Divide $115 \div 2$.

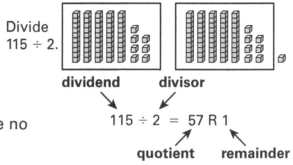

dividend   divisor

$$115 \div 2 = 57 \text{ R } 1$$

quotient   remainder

Think

Use ___3___ hundreds, ___2___ tens, and ___3___ ones to show 323.

Divide the blocks into ___3___ equal groups.

Find how many __hundreds__, __tens__, and __ones__ are in each group.

Connect

Separate the blocks into 3 equal groups.

Regroup the 2 tens as 20 ones. Now there are 23 ones.

Separate the 23 ones into 3 equal groups.

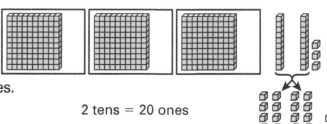

2 tens = 20 ones

Look at each group. There are 107 in each group, with 2 left over. The quotient is 107, with a remainder of 2.

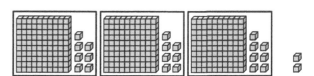

There are no tens blocks, so there is a 0 in the tens place of the quotient.

Let's Talk

How is the quotient of 107 different than a quotient of 17?
What does the zero in 107 represent?

Fill in the blanks. Solve the problem.

Sunni is dividing 613 quarters equally among 3 jars.

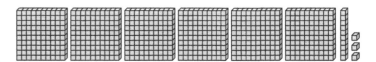

How many quarters are in each jar?

■ What blocks are used to model 613?

_____ hundreds, _____ ten, and _____ ones

■ Draw a model to divide the hundreds into _____ equal groups.

> For any division problem, the remainder must be less than the divisor. Otherwise, you could keep dividing among the equal groups.

■ There are not enough tens to be split among the groups. So, there are _____ tens in each group. Regroup the leftover ten as _____ ones.

■ There are _____ ones in all. Draw to divide the ones into equal groups.

Solution: There are _____ quarters in each jar, and there is _____ left over.

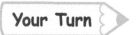
Your Turn — **Now, use what you know to solve this problem.**

1. Use these blocks to help you divide 562 into 4 equal groups. How much is in each group? Draw a model.

    Ⓐ 104 R 2
    Ⓑ 140 R 0
    Ⓒ 140 R 2
    Ⓓ 142 R 0

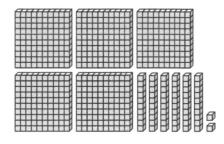

 When do you write zero in the quotient?

Explore

When you use models to divide 3-digit numbers, you find how many hundreds, tens, and ones are in the quotient. If there are no tens or ones, use a 0 for that place.

How can you find a quotient that has a zero without using models? 843 ÷ 4

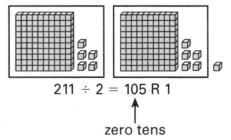

211 ÷ 2 = 105 R 1

↑
zero tens

Think

Divide 843 by 4. Divide __843__ into __4__ equal groups.
Find how many __hundreds__, __tens__, and __ones__ are in each group.
843 has __8__ hundreds, __4__ tens, and __3__ ones.

Connect

Follow these steps to find 4)843 using **long division**.

1. *Divide* 8 hundreds into 4 equal groups. Write 2 in the quotient. *Multiply* 2 hundreds by the divisor, 4. Write 800 and *subtract*.

$$\begin{array}{r} x\,-\,2 \\ 4\overline{)843} \\ -800 \\ \hline 43 \end{array}$$

2. *Divide* 4 tens into 4 equal groups. Write 1 in the quotient. *Multiply* 1 ten by 4. Write 40 and *subtract*.

$$\begin{array}{r} x\,-\,21 \\ 4\overline{)843} \\ -800 \\ \hline 43 \\ -40 \\ \hline 3 \end{array}$$

3. *Divide* 3 ones into 4 equal groups.

Since you cannot divide 3 ones into 4 groups, write 0 in the ones place. *Multiply* 0 by 4 and *subtract*.

The 3 left over is the remainder.

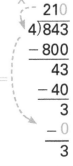

$$\begin{array}{r} x\,-\,210 \\ 4\overline{)843} \\ -800 \\ \hline 43 \\ -40 \\ \hline 3 \\ -0 \\ \hline 3 \end{array}$$

The quotient is 210, with a remainder of 3. Write 843 ÷ 4 = 210 R 3.

Let's Talk

When should you write a 0 in the quotient of a division problem? Give an example of a division problem that has no zeros in the quotient.

Fill in the blanks. Solve the problem.

Carolina is separating 548 cans among 5 recycling bins equally.

How many cans are in each bin?

- Divide _____ into _____ equal groups.

  548 has _____ hundreds, _____ tens, and _____ ones.

- Write the problem. ⬚)⬚

  Divide 5 hundreds into _____ equal groups. ⟶ ⬚)⬚
  Write _____ in the quotient.   −⬚

  Divide 4 tens into _____ equal groups. ⟶   48
  Write _____ in the quotient.   −⬚

  Divide 48 ones into _____ equal groups. ⟶   48
  Write _____ in the quotient.   −⬚
                                                   3

- The quotient is _____, with a remainder of _____.

  Write _____ R _____.

Solution: Each bin has _____ cans, and there are _____ left over.

> Not all division problems will have a zero in the quotient. When dividing a 3-digit number, only write a 0 when tens or ones are not great enough to divide into equal groups.

Your Turn ▷ **Now, use what you know to solve this problem.**

2. Bookstore employees choose a total of 325 books to put on display. They divide the books evenly among 8 shelves. How many books are on each shelf?

   Show your work.

   There are _____ books on each shelf, with _____ books left over.

Solve the problem. Then read why each answer choice is correct or not correct.

A DVD manufacturer is packing 621 DVDs into 3 large boxes, with the same number of DVDs in each box. How many DVDs will be in each box?

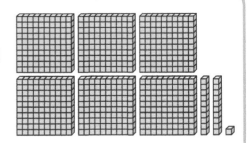

Ⓐ 270, 1 left over   Ⓒ 207, 0 left over

Ⓑ 207, 1 left over   Ⓓ 27, 0 left over

Check

Check to see if you chose the correct answer.

To find the number of DVDs in each box, divide 621 by 3.

Divide the 6 hundreds into 3 groups. There are 2 hundreds in each group.

There are 2 tens. Since the tens cannot be divided into 3 groups, regroup the tens as 20 ones. Now, there are 21 ones.

Divide the 21 ones into 3 groups. There are 7 ones in each group.

There are 0 ones left over.

So, the correct answer is Ⓒ.

Why are the other answer choices not correct?

Ⓐ 270, 1 left over	There are 0 tens in each group, so write a zero in the tens place of the quotient, not the ones place.
Ⓑ 207, 1 left over	The remainder is the number left over, not the number of ones in the dividend.
Ⓓ 27, 0 left over	There are 0 tens in each group, not 2. A zero is needed in the tens place of the quotient.

- Regroup as needed if you can't divide evenly into groups.
- Carefully write each number of the quotient in the correct place value, using 0 when the tens or ones are not great enough to divide into the groups.
- Check for a remainder and record it.

3. Which place will have to be regrouped, if any, in the following problem?

$$3\overline{)692}$$

Ⓐ hundreds

Ⓑ tens

Ⓒ ones

Ⓓ none

4. Steven modeled 281 using base-ten blocks.

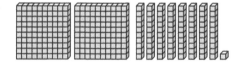

He divides the blocks into 4 equal groups. What are the quotient and remainder?

Ⓐ 20 R 0

Ⓑ 70 R 0

Ⓒ 70 R 1

Ⓓ 120 R 1

5. Which division problem is shown by the model of a quotient and remainder?

 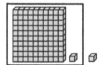

Ⓐ $2\overline{)201}$

Ⓑ $2\overline{)203}$

Ⓒ $203\overline{)2}$

Ⓓ $2\overline{)101}$

6. Jonah is helping to set up chairs for the school play. There are 530 chairs, and he places them in rows of 5 chairs each. How many rows will there be?

Ⓐ 16

Ⓑ 100 R 6

Ⓒ 106

Ⓓ 160

Study the model. It is a good example of a written answer.

Student Model

Show

Luther is separating 522 baseballs into 4 equal groups. How many baseballs will be in each group? How many are left over?

Use a model and long division to show your work.

Model

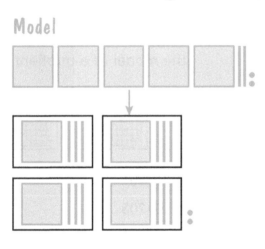

Long Division

$$
\begin{array}{r}
130 \\
4\overline{)522} \\
-400 \\
\hline
122 \\
-120 \\
\hline
2 \\
-0 \\
\hline
2
\end{array}
$$

☑ The student shows each step.

Solution: 130 baseballs, with 2 left over

☑ The student correctly answers the question asked.

Explain

Explain how you got your answer.

First, I drew a model of the dividend using base-ten blocks. The divisor is 4, so I separated the blocks into 4 equal groups. I divided the hundreds and regrouped the leftover hundred as 10 tens. Next, I divided the tens. There are only 2 ones, not enough to divide among the 4 groups, so I wrote a 0 in the ones place of the quotient. The remainder is 2. I got the same answer using both ways of dividing.

☑ The student gives important details about how to find the quotient and remainder.

☑ The student uses the math words *dividend*, *divisor*, *regroup*, *quotient*, and *remainder*.

7. Marissa has 621 craft sticks to divide evenly among 3 art classes. How many craft sticks should she give to each class? Are there any left over?

Use a model and long division to show you work.

Solution: _____

Explain how you got your answer.

_____

_____

_____

_____

_____

As you solve division problems, remember to
- draw pictures to show equal groups.
- carefully regroup numbers as needed.
- write a 0 in the quotient when the tens or ones are not great enough to divide into the groups.
- use multiplication to check your answer.

Solve each problem.

8. What division problem is shown by the model of a quotient and remainder?

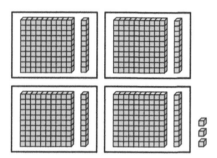

Ⓐ $4\overline{)113}$

Ⓑ $443\overline{)4}$

Ⓒ $3\overline{)443}$

Ⓓ $4\overline{)443}$

9. A manufacturer has 843 cases of crackers to load into 4 trucks. How many cases will be in each truck? How many are left over?

Ⓐ 201 cases, 0 left over

Ⓑ 201 cases, 3 left over

Ⓒ 210 cases, 0 left over

Ⓓ 210 cases, 3 left over

10. An after-school club has raised $873 to give equally to 3 charities. How much is in each donation?

Ⓐ $221

Ⓑ $231

Ⓒ $290

Ⓓ $291

11. A warehouse worker is packaging 954 video games into boxes. Each box holds 5 games. How many boxes does he need for all the games?

Ⓐ 191

Ⓑ 190

Ⓒ 111

Ⓓ 110

12. What is the remainder when 623 is divided by 6?

Ⓐ 5

Ⓑ 4

Ⓒ 3

Ⓓ 0

13. Kevin is separating 587 building blocks equally into 7 bags. How many blocks will be in each bag? How many blocks will be left over?

Ⓐ 83 blocks, 0 left over

Ⓑ 83 blocks, 6 left over

Ⓒ 803 blocks, 6 left over

Ⓓ 830 blocks, 6 left over

14. Tameka works at a craft store. She has to separate 274 coils of yarn equally among 9 shelves. She plans to buy the leftover coils to make a scarf.

Write the division problem and divide.

How many coils will Tameka buy?

_____

15. Miranda and two of her friends are taking a trip. They will drive a total of 315 miles, and each will drive an equal amount. How many miles will each person drive?

Use pictures, words, or numbers to show your work.

Solution: _____

Explain how you found your answer.

_____

_____

_____

_____

 **How can you divide by 2-digit divisors?**

Explore

You can use **long division** to divide by a 1-digit number.

How can you divide if the divisor is a 2-digit number?

$575 \div 22$

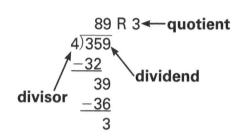

Think

The problem $575 \div 22$ means divide __575__ into groups of __22__.

Find the number of groups.

First, estimate the quotient. Round the dividend and divisor, and divide.

575 is about __600__.   22 is a little more than __20__.

__600__ $\div$ __20__ $=$ __30__   The quotient should be close to __30__.

Connect

Then find the exact quotient. Set up the problem. $22\overline{)575}$
Use long division to solve.

$$\begin{array}{r} 26 \text{ R } 3 \\ 22\overline{)575} \\ -44\downarrow \\ \hline 135 \\ -132 \\ \hline 3 \end{array}$$

There are two 22s in 57. Write 2 in the quotient above the 7.
$2 \times 22 = 44$, so write 44 under 57.
Subtract and write the difference, 13. Bring down the 5.

There are six 22s in 135. Write 6 in the quotient.
Subtract and write the difference, 3.
Write the quotient with the **remainder**, or the amount left over.

The quotient is 26 R 3.

Compare it to the estimate. It is close to the estimate, 30.

Let's Talk

Why was it helpful to estimate the quotient before finding the exact answer?

Fill in the blanks. Solve the problem.

A baker bakes 288 biscuits. Each baking sheet holds 24 biscuits. How many baking sheets does he fill?

■ Divide _____ into groups of _____. Find the number of groups.

■ Round the dividend and divisor.

288 is almost _____.   24 is a little more than _____.

Estimate the quotient.   _____ ÷ _____ = _____.

The quotient should be close to _____.

■ Set up the problem. Then use long division to solve.

Record each step.

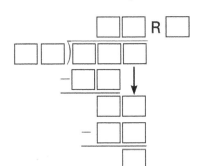

> There is one 24 in 28. Write 1 in the quotient above the 8.
>
> 1 × 24 = 24, so write 24 under 28.
>
> Subtract and write the difference, 4. Bring down the 8.
>
> Repeat these steps for dividing 48 by 24.

> To estimate, round each number to the greatest place value.
>
> 623 to the nearest hundred:
> 653 → 700
>
> 52 to the nearest ten:
> 52 → 50

Solution: The baker uses _____ baking sheets, with _____ biscuits left over.

Your Turn   **Now, use what you know to solve this problem.**

1. A pet store received an order of 592 fish. An employee separates the fish into different tanks. Each tank can hold 31 fish. How many tanks will the employee fill? How many fish are left over?

Ⓐ 20 tanks, 0 fish left over

Ⓑ 19 tanks, 3 fish left over

Ⓒ 19 tanks, 0 fish left over

Ⓓ 18 tanks, 4 fish left over

How can you interpret remainders to solve division problems?

Explore

You can use **division** to solve problems when an amount is being separated into equal groups.

Mrs. Stone is reading an 894-page book. She reads 27 pages each day. How many days will it take Mrs. Stone to read the whole book?

How does the remainder affect the answer to the problem?

Think

The problem means divide ___894___ into groups of ___27___.

Find the number of groups.

Set up the problem.   27)‾894‾

Connect

Use long division to solve. Then interpret the remainder in the quotient.

```
      33 R 3
  27)894
   − 81↓
      84
    − 81
       3
```

There are three 27s in 89. Write 3 in the quotient above the 9.
3 × 27 = 81, so write 81 under 89.
Subtract and write the difference, 8. Bring down the 4.

There are three 27s in 84. Write 3 in the quotient.
Subtract and write the difference, 3.

The result is 33 R 3. This means that after 33 days, Mrs. Stone will still need to read 3 pages. Because 33 days will not be enough time, she needs 34 days to finish the book.

In this problem, the remainder increases the answer by 1.

Let's Talk

Why is 34 a better answer to this problem than 33 R 3?

Fill in the blanks. Solve the problem.

A librarian is placing 881 books on shelves. If each shelf can hold 38 books, how many shelves can she fill completely?

■ The problem asks for the number of shelves that can be filled completely.

■ Divide _____ into groups of _____. Find the number of groups.

■ Set up the problem. Then, use long division to solve.

Divide, multiply, subtract, bring down, and repeat.

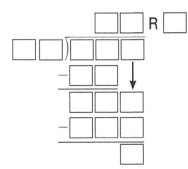

The result of the division is _____ R _____.

■ The quotient means that _____ shelves can be completely filled.

The remainder means that _____ books will not fit on the shelves.

You need to _____ the remainder.

Solution: She can fill _____ shelves completely.

> When reading division word problems, pay close attention to the question.
>
> Sometimes you are asked to find the remainder or the quotient *and* remainder. Other times, you need to figure out how the remainder affects the quotient.

Your Turn ▷ **Now, use what you know to solve this problem.**

2. Mr. Guerrero is buying supplies for the school picnic. He knows that 672 people will be at the picnic. Plates come in packs of 36. How many packs of plates should Mr. Guerrero buy? Show your work.

672 ÷ 36 = _____

He should buy _____ packs of plates.

Solve the problem. Then read why each answer choice is correct or not correct.

Solve

A group of 336 students signs up for a trip to the aquarium. Each bus holds 52 passengers. How many buses are needed to transport all of the students on the trip?

- Ⓐ   6 buses
- Ⓑ   7 buses
- Ⓒ   24 buses
- Ⓓ   61 buses

Check

Check to see if you chose the correct answer.

Find how many groups of 52 are in 336. Divide 336 by 52.

```
        6 R 24
52)336
   − 312
      24
```

The quotient of 6 R 24 means that 6 buses are filled, but 24 people are left over. This means 6 buses are not enough to transport all of the students.

The remainder increases the answer by 1. The group will need 7 buses.

So, the correct answer is Ⓑ.

Why are the other answer choices not correct?

Ⓐ 6 buses	This is the number of buses that are filled.
Ⓒ 24 buses	This is the remainder, or the number of people left over.
Ⓓ 61 buses	The 6 in the quotient represents 6 ones, not 6 tens.

Solve each problem. Use the hints to avoid mistakes.

- Identify the total and the number in each group or the number of groups.
- Use long division. Record each step.
- Decide if the remainder affects the solution of the problem. Ask yourself: Does the remainder increase the answer? Is the remainder the answer? Can the remainder be ignored?

3. Kris works in a hardware store. She sold 864 packets of nails last month. There are 32 packets of nails in each box. How many boxes of nails did Kris sell?

Ⓐ 27

Ⓑ 28

Ⓒ 30

Ⓓ 32

4. How many equal groups of 41 are in 847?

Ⓐ 20

Ⓑ 21

Ⓒ 27

Ⓓ 28

5. Mr. Li is setting up for the spring band concert. He has 582 chairs to place in equal rows. He places 36 chairs in each row. How many chairs are left over?

Ⓐ 17 chairs

Ⓑ 16 chairs

Ⓒ 6 chairs

Ⓓ 0 chairs

6. Which division problem has a quotient of 52?

Ⓐ 632 ÷ 21 =

Ⓑ 572 ÷ 52 =

Ⓒ 387 ÷ 43 =

Ⓓ 988 ÷ 19 =

Study the model. It is a good example of a written answer.

Student Model

Show

Katy took 493 pictures with her digital camera. She prints the pictures and organizes them in albums. Each album can hold 48 pictures. How many albums does Katy need to display all of her pictures?

Use pictures, words, or numbers to show your work.

Estimate. $500 \div 50 = 10$

Divide.

$$\begin{array}{r} 10 \text{ R } 13 \\ 48\overline{)493} \\ -48\downarrow \\ \hline 13 \\ -0 \\ \hline 13 \end{array}$$

10 albums can only hold 10×48 pictures $= 480$ pictures.
She needs 1 more album to hold all 493 pictures.

Solution: Katy needs __11__ photo albums.

Explain

Explain how you got your answer.

First, I estimated by rounding each number to its

greatest place value and dividing: $500 \div 50 = 10$.

Then, I used long division to find the exact quotient

and remainder: 10 R 13. This means that if Katy fills

10 albums, she would have 13 pictures left over.

10 albums would not be enough, so she needs 11 albums

for all the pictures.

☑ The student shows each step.

☑ The student correctly answers the question asked.

☑ The student gives important details about how to find the answer.

☑ The student uses the math words *estimate*, *long division*, *quotient*, and *remainder*.

7. Brent is saving money to buy a new bicycle.
The bicycle costs $381. If he saves $26 each week,
how many weeks until he can buy the bicycle?

Use pictures, words, or numbers to show your work.

CHECKLIST

Did you . . .

☐ show each step?

☐ answer the question asked?

☐ give important details?

☐ use math words?

Solution: Brent needs to save for _____ weeks to buy the bicycle.

Explain how you got your answer.

_____

_____

_____

_____

_____

As you solve division problems, remember to
- determine exactly what the question is asking.
- estimate the quotient first.
- write out each step of the long division.
- use multiplication and addition to check your work.

Solve each problem.

8. Maria works in a café. She orders 336 cups. There are 24 cups in each pack. How many packs of cups does Maria order?

Ⓐ 11 packs

Ⓑ 14 packs

Ⓒ 15 packs

Ⓓ 24 packs

9. What is 876 ÷ 32?

Ⓐ 30

Ⓑ 27 R 22

Ⓒ 27 R 12

Ⓓ 27

10. Jackson is tiling his basement floor. The floor is 459 square feet. Each box of tiles covers 18 square feet. How many boxes of tiles should Jackson order?

Ⓐ 9 boxes

Ⓑ 19 boxes

Ⓒ 25 boxes

Ⓓ 26 boxes

11. The art teacher has $350 to spend on craft kits. Each kit costs $16. How many craft kits can the art teacher buy?

Ⓐ 14 kits

Ⓑ 20 kits

Ⓒ 21 kits

Ⓓ 22 kits

12. The Smith family is driving 812 miles from Pennsylvania to Georgia. They drive 58 miles each hour. How many hours will they spend driving?

Ⓐ 13 hours

Ⓑ 14 hours

Ⓒ 15 hours

Ⓓ 16 hours

13. What is the remainder when 784 is divided by 19?

Ⓐ 0

Ⓑ 5

Ⓒ 6

Ⓓ 7

14. The baseball team raised $387 to buy new baseball bats. Each baseball bat costs $63. Find how many baseball bats the team can buy. How much money will the team have left over? Show your work.

_____ bats

$ _____ left over

15. Regi and his brothers mow lawns during the summer. They earn $24 for each lawn. How many lawns do they have to mow to earn enough money to buy a riding lawn mower for $999?

Use pictures, words, or numbers to show your work.

Solution: They have to mow _____ lawns to earn enough money.

Explain how you found your answer.

_____

_____

_____

_____

PART ONE: Learn About Mixed Numbers

 **?** How can you rename improper fractions as mixed numbers?

Explore

You can use a **fraction** to show part of a whole. When the numerator and denominator are the same, the fraction equals 1 whole.

numerator $\longrightarrow$
denominator $\longrightarrow$ $\quad \frac{5}{5} = 1 \qquad \frac{1}{1} = 1 \qquad \frac{9}{9} = 1 \qquad \frac{20}{20} = 1$

How can you name amounts that are greater than 1 whole?

Think

Look at these models. They show the same amount.

$\boxed{\frac{1}{3}}\boxed{\frac{1}{3}}\boxed{\frac{1}{3}}\;\boxed{\frac{1}{3}}\boxed{\frac{1}{3}}\boxed{\frac{1}{3}}\;\boxed{\frac{1}{3}}\square\square$ $\qquad$ $\boxed{1}\quad\boxed{1}\quad\boxed{\frac{1}{3}}\square\square$

Each whole is divided into __thirds__.

There are __7__ thirds in all. Write $\frac{7}{3}$.

This is an **improper fraction** because the numerator is greater than or equal to the denominator.

There are __2__ wholes plus __1__ third.

Write $2\frac{1}{3}$.

This is a **mixed number** because it has a whole number and a fraction.

$\frac{7}{3}$ and $2\frac{1}{3}$ show the same amount. $\frac{7}{3} = 2\frac{1}{3}$

Connect

To **rename** an improper fraction, divide the numerator by the denominator. The quotient is the whole number. The remainder is the numerator of the fraction.

$\frac{7}{3}$
$\begin{array}{r} 2 \\ 3\overline{)7} \\ -6 \\ \hline 1 \end{array}$ 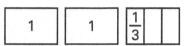 number of wholes

number of thirds

Write $2\frac{1}{3}$.

Let's Talk

How are $\frac{22}{5}$ and $4\frac{2}{5}$ different? How are they similar?

Fill in the blanks. Solve the problem.

Tyler had cookie cakes at his birthday party.
He and his friends ate the shaded amount shown below.

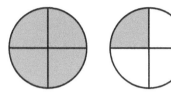

How can you show this amount as an improper fraction and a mixed number?

■ Each whole is divided into _____.

There are _____ fourths in all.

Write the improper fraction. $\dfrac{\square}{\square}$

■ Use division to write the mixed number.

4) 5   There is _____ whole.

There is _____ fourth.

The mixed number is $\square\dfrac{\square}{\square}$.

Solution: Tyler and his friends ate _____ or _____ of the cookie cakes.

> Count the number of parts in each whole. This is the denominator of the improper fraction as well as the fraction in the mixed number.

Your Turn   **Now, use what you know to solve this problem.**

1. Imani used $\dfrac{8}{5}$ cans of paint for her bedroom.
    Which mixed number shows the same amount?

    (A) $\dfrac{3}{8}$ (C) $1\dfrac{2}{8}$

    (B) $1\dfrac{3}{5}$ (D) $2\dfrac{2}{5}$

How can you rename mixed numbers in multiple ways?

Explore

You can use a mixed number and an improper fraction to name the same fraction that is greater than 1, such as $2\frac{1}{4}$ and $\frac{9}{4}$.

How can you write different names for the same amount shown by a mixed number?

Think

$2\frac{1}{4}$ is a mixed number because it has a __whole number__ and a __fraction__.

The mixed number $2\frac{1}{4}$ represents __2__ wholes plus __$\frac{1}{4}$__.

Connect

Rename $2\frac{1}{4}$.

Because 1 whole equals 4 fourths, you can regroup 1 whole as 4 fourths and combine 4 fourths with the fraction. You can rename the mixed number $2\frac{1}{4}$ twice.

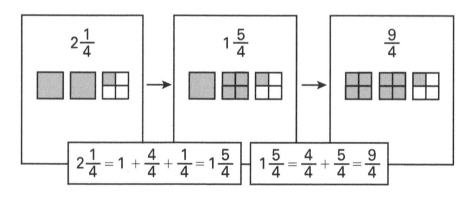

$$2\frac{1}{4} = 1 + \frac{4}{4} + \frac{1}{4} = 1\frac{5}{4} \qquad 1\frac{5}{4} = \frac{4}{4} + \frac{5}{4} = \frac{9}{4}$$

When you rename a number, the value does not change.

Let's Talk

Why is $6\frac{4}{7}$ the same as $6 + \frac{4}{7}$? Explain using a model and a math sentence.

Fill in the blanks. Solve the problem.

Abigail makes quilts by sewing separate pieces of fabric together. She has finished $2\frac{3}{8}$ quilts.

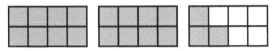

How can you rename this amount as an improper fraction?

■ The mixed number $2\frac{3}{8}$ represents _____ wholes plus _____.

■ Because _____ whole equals _____ eighths, you can regroup 1 whole as 8 eighths and combine 8 eighths with the fraction.

$$2\frac{3}{8} = \boxed{} + \frac{\boxed{}}{8} + \frac{\boxed{}}{8} = \boxed{}\frac{\boxed{}}{8}$$

$$1\frac{11}{8} = \frac{\boxed{}}{8} + \frac{\boxed{}}{8} = \frac{\boxed{}}{8}$$

Solution: Abigail finished _____ quilts in all.

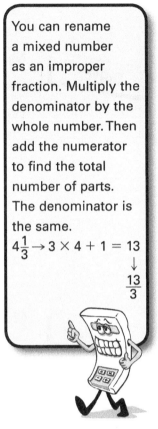

You can rename a mixed number as an improper fraction. Multiply the denominator by the whole number. Then add the numerator to find the total number of parts. The denominator is the same.

$$4\frac{1}{3} \rightarrow 3 \times 4 + 1 = 13$$
$$\downarrow$$
$$\frac{13}{3}$$

Your Turn ▷ **Now, use what you know to solve this problem.**

2. Raylan fills $2\frac{2}{5}$ racks with magazines at the library. What improper fraction names the same number of racks? Use regrouping, or multiplication and addition.

$$2\frac{2}{5} = \underline{}$$

Solve the problem. Then read why each answer choice is correct or not correct.

Solve

Mr. Archer is making large square mosaics for his walkway out of smaller square tiles. So far, he has finished $4\frac{5}{9}$ large square mosaics. Which number is equivalent to $4\frac{5}{9}$?

Ⓐ 4   Ⓒ $\frac{29}{9}$

Ⓑ 5   Ⓓ $\frac{41}{9}$

Check

Check to see if you chose the correct answer.

Multiply the denominator by the whole number. Then add the numerator to find the total number of parts. The denominator is the same.

$$4\frac{5}{9} \rightarrow 4 \times 9 + 5 = 41 \rightarrow \frac{41}{9}$$

The model shows 4 whole mosaics, each divided into ninths.
4 groups × 9 ninths = 36 ninths

The model shows 5 extra ninths in the last mosaic.
36 ninths + 5 ninths = 41 ninths

There are $\frac{41}{9}$.

So, the correct answer is Ⓓ.

Why are the other answer choices not correct?

Ⓐ 4	There are more than 4 whole mosaics.
Ⓑ 5	There are not enough small squares to make 5 wholes.
Ⓒ $\frac{29}{9}$	The whole number was multiplied by the numerator instead of the denominator. Multiply the whole number by the denominator and add the numerator. This will give the numerator of the improper fraction.

Your Turn ⟩ Solve each problem. Use the hints to avoid mistakes.

- Draw a model if one is not given.
- Use division to write an improper fraction as a mixed number.
- Use multiplication and addition to write a mixed number as an improper fraction.
- The denominator of an improper fraction and the fraction in the corresponding mixed number should be the same.

3. Anisha is entering 3 paintings in the art show. So far she has completed $2\frac{1}{4}$ paintings.

Which improper fraction names the number of paintings she has completed?

Ⓐ $\frac{1}{4}$ painting

Ⓑ $\frac{3}{4}$ painting

Ⓒ $\frac{9}{4}$ paintings

Ⓓ $\frac{12}{4}$ paintings

4. What is $\frac{7}{3}$ written as a mixed number?

Ⓐ $\frac{4}{3}$

Ⓑ $1\frac{1}{3}$

Ⓒ $1\frac{3}{7}$

Ⓓ $2\frac{1}{3}$

5. Marcus made mini-cakes in the pans below. He filled $\frac{11}{6}$ pans with batter.

Which number also names the portion of the pans that are filled?

Ⓐ $\frac{5}{6}$

Ⓑ $1\frac{5}{6}$

Ⓒ $1\frac{5}{5}$

Ⓓ $2\frac{1}{5}$

6. Which improper fraction names the same amount as $1\frac{7}{8}$?

Ⓐ $\frac{15}{8}$

Ⓑ $\frac{13}{8}$

Ⓒ $\frac{9}{8}$

Ⓓ $\frac{1}{8}$

Study the model. It is a good example of a written answer.

Student Model

Show

A school is painting classrooms throughout the building. The painters have completed $4\frac{1}{6}$ classrooms.

How can you rename the amount the painters have completed as two different mixed numbers?

Use pictures, words, or numbers to show your work.

1 whole = 6 sixths

$4\frac{1}{6} = 3 + \frac{6}{6} + \frac{1}{6} = 3\frac{7}{6}$

$3\frac{7}{6} = 2 + \frac{6}{6} + \frac{7}{6} = 2\frac{13}{6}$

> ☑ The student shows each step.

Solution: The school has painted _$3\frac{7}{6}$_ or _$2\frac{13}{6}$_ classrooms.

> ☑ The student correctly answers the question asked.

Explain

Explain how you got your answer.

The mixed number $4\frac{1}{6}$ means 4 wholes plus $\frac{1}{6}$. Because

1 whole equals 6 sixths, I can regroup 1 whole as

6 sixths and combine it with the fraction. First,

I renamed $4\frac{1}{6}$ as $3\frac{7}{6}$. Then, I renamed $3\frac{7}{6}$ as $2\frac{13}{6}$.

So, $4\frac{1}{6}$ is the same as the mixed numbers $3\frac{7}{6}$

and $2\frac{13}{6}$. I drew a model to show $3\frac{7}{6}$ and a model to

show $2\frac{13}{6}$. The model shows they are equal.

> ☑ The student gives important details about how to find the answer.

> ☑ The student uses the math words *mixed number*, *regroup*, *fraction*, and *rename*.

7. Mrs. Torres drives $3\frac{7}{10}$ miles each day to school.

   How can you rename how far she drives as two different mixed numbers?

   Use pictures, words, or numbers to show your work.

Solution: Mrs. Torres drives _____ or _____ miles each day.

Explain how you got your answer.

_____

_____

_____

_____

_____

_____

As you solve problems with improper fractions and mixed numbers, remember to
- use a model to compare numbers that name an amount.
- use operations to rename numbers.
- use a different method to check your work.

Solve each problem.

8. Elonzo filled $\frac{7}{2}$ boxes with classroom supplies. Which mixed number describes the number of boxes he filled?

   Ⓐ $2\frac{1}{2}$ Ⓒ $3\frac{1}{2}$

   Ⓑ $3\frac{2}{7}$ Ⓓ $4\frac{1}{4}$

9. Which improper fraction names the same amount as $2\frac{5}{6}$?

   Ⓐ $\frac{6}{3}$ Ⓒ $\frac{12}{6}$

   Ⓑ $\frac{17}{6}$ Ⓓ $\frac{18}{6}$

10. Noel played in $3\frac{1}{3}$ volleyball games in gym class. Which of the following numbers represents the same amount?

    Ⓐ $\frac{4}{6}$ Ⓒ $1\frac{4}{3}$

    Ⓑ $\frac{7}{3}$ Ⓓ $1\frac{7}{3}$

11. Naoki has a piece of yarn that is $\frac{40}{9}$ feet long. Which is **not** the same length as her piece of yarn?

    Ⓐ $1\frac{31}{9}$

    Ⓑ $2\frac{22}{9}$

    Ⓒ $3\frac{13}{9}$

    Ⓓ $4\frac{5}{9}$

12. Theo drew 3 rectangles. He divided each rectangle into 6 equal parts and shaded $2\frac{1}{6}$ rectangles. Which of these is another way to name the shaded amount?

    Ⓐ $6\frac{1}{2}$

    Ⓑ $2\frac{13}{6}$

    Ⓒ $1\frac{7}{6}$

    Ⓓ $\frac{9}{6}$

13. A baseball game lasted $2\frac{3}{4}$ hours. Which number names the same amount of hours?

Ⓐ $\frac{9}{4}$

Ⓑ $\frac{11}{4}$

Ⓒ $\frac{14}{4}$

Ⓓ $\frac{24}{4}$

14. Aubrey made three chicken pies. She gave $\frac{23}{8}$ pies to her neighbors.

Write two mixed numbers to show the amount of pie given to the neighbors. Show your work.

Solution:

_____ and _____

15. Samantha used $4\frac{1}{6}$ cartons of eggs to make brownies for the bake sale. How can you rename the number of cartons she used as an improper fraction?

Use pictures, words, or numbers to show your work.

Solution: Samantha used _____ cartons of eggs.

Explain how you found your answer.

_____

_____

_____

_____

PART ONE: Learn About Adding Like Fractions

How can you add like fractions?

Explore

A **fraction** compares a part to a whole. This model shows $\frac{4}{10}$ because there are 10 equal parts in the whole, and there are 4 parts shaded.

numerator ⟶ $\frac{4}{10}$
denominator ⟶

How can you find the sum of two like fractions?

Think

Like fractions have the same denominator. They represent parts of wholes that are divided into the same number of equal parts. $\frac{4}{10}$ and $\frac{3}{10}$ are like fractions.

Add. $\frac{4}{10} + \frac{3}{10}$

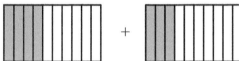

Use fraction models.

Each model is divided into __10__ equal parts, or __tenths__.

The first model has __4__ parts shaded, and the second model has __3__ parts shaded.

To add, count the number of parts shaded in all.

There are __7__ tenths shaded in all.

Connect

To find the sum, keep the same denominator, because there are still 10 parts in one whole. Add the numerators to find how many parts in all.

So, $\frac{4}{10} + \frac{3}{10} = \frac{7}{10}$.

Why do $\frac{4}{10} + \frac{3}{10}$ and $\frac{3}{10} + \frac{4}{10}$ have the same sum?

Fill in the blanks. Solve the problem.

Annie ate $\frac{1}{8}$ of a pizza. Her brother ate $\frac{3}{8}$ of another pizza.

The pizzas are the same size.

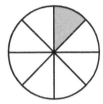 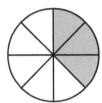

How much pizza did they eat in all?

- Each pizza is divided into _____ equal parts, or _____.

- The first pizza has _____ part shaded.

    The second pizza has _____ parts shaded.

    There are _____ eighths shaded in all.

- Add. $\dfrac{\square}{8} + \dfrac{\square}{8} = \dfrac{\square}{8}$

- Simplify the answer.

    $\dfrac{4 \div 4}{8 \div 4} = \dfrac{\square}{\square}$

Solution: They ate _____ of a pizza.

> You can simplify a fraction by dividing the numerator and denominator by the **greatest common factor (GCF)**. The GCF is the greatest factor that the numbers have in common.

Your Turn **Now, use what you know to solve this problem.**

1. What is the sum of $\frac{3}{6}$ and $\frac{1}{6}$?
   Simplify the answer.

   Ⓐ $\frac{1}{3}$

   Ⓑ $\frac{2}{4}$

   Ⓒ $\frac{2}{3}$

   Ⓓ $\frac{2}{2}$

How can you subtract like fractions?

Explore

To find the sum of two like fractions, you add the numerators and keep the same denominator.

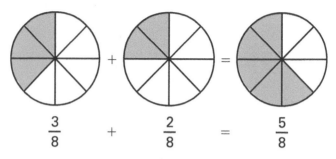

$$\frac{3}{8} \quad + \quad \frac{2}{8} \quad = \quad \frac{5}{8}$$

How can you find the difference of two like fractions?

Think

Find the difference. Subtract. $\frac{4}{5} - \frac{3}{5}$

Use a model.

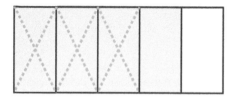

The model shows __4__ fifths.

There are __5__ equal parts in all, and __4__ parts are shaded.

To subtract, cross out __3__ fifths.

There is __1__ fifth left over.

Connect

To find the difference, subtract the numerators to show how many parts are left. Keep the same denominator because there are still 5 parts in one whole.

So, $\frac{4}{5} - \frac{3}{5} = \frac{1}{5}$.

Let's Talk

Is $\frac{4}{5} - \frac{3}{5}$ the same as $\frac{3}{5} - \frac{4}{5}$? Explain.

Fill in the blanks. Solve the problem.

Heidi lives $\frac{1}{8}$ mile from Shady Park. José lives $\frac{6}{8}$ mile from the park.

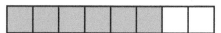

How much closer does Heidi live to the park than José?

- Find the difference.

  Subtract. $\frac{\boxed{}}{8} - \frac{\boxed{}}{8}$

- The model shows _____ eighths.

  There are _____ equal parts in all, and _____ parts are shaded.

  To subtract, cross out _____ eighth.

  There are _____ eighths left over.

- So, $\frac{6}{8} - \frac{1}{8} = \frac{\boxed{}}{\boxed{}}$. This fraction cannot be simplified.

Solution: Heidi lives _____ mile closer to Shady Park than José.

> If a fraction cannot be simplified, it is in **simplest form**. If the only common factor of a numerator and denominator is 1, then the fraction is in simplest form.

Your Turn Now, use what you know to solve this problem.

2. What is the difference of $\frac{8}{10}$ and $\frac{4}{10}$? Simplify the answer.

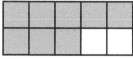

$$\frac{8}{10} - \frac{4}{10} = \frac{\boxed{}}{\boxed{}}$$

$$\frac{\boxed{} \div 2}{\boxed{} \div 2} = \frac{\boxed{}}{\boxed{}}$$

Solve the problem. Then read why each answer choice is correct or not correct.

Solve

Mr. Marshall needs $\frac{3}{4}$ pound of turkey for a recipe.
He has only $\frac{1}{4}$ pound of turkey.

How much more turkey does he need?

Ⓐ $\frac{1}{4}$ pound   Ⓒ $\frac{2}{3}$ pound

Ⓑ $\frac{1}{2}$ pound   Ⓓ $\frac{4}{4}$ pound

Check

Check to see if you chose the correct answer.

Subtract. $\frac{3}{4} - \frac{1}{4}$

Subtract the numerators to show how many parts are left.

Keep the same denominator. $\frac{3}{4} - \frac{1}{4} = \frac{2}{4}$

Simplify by dividing the numerator and denominator by their greatest

common factor (GCF), 2. $\frac{2 \div 2}{4 \div 2} = \frac{1}{2}$

So, the correct answer is Ⓑ.

Why are the other answer choices not correct?

Ⓐ $\frac{1}{4}$ pound	This amount should be subtracted from the amount he needs.
Ⓒ $\frac{2}{3}$ pound	The denominator should stay the same.
Ⓓ $\frac{4}{4}$ pound	The fractions should be subtracted, not added.

Your Turn

Solve each problem. Use the hints to avoid mistakes.

- Decide if you need to add or subtract.
- Identify the fractions and write the problem.
- Add or subtract the numerators.
- Simplify the answer if you can.

3. Alan poured $\frac{1}{3}$ cup flour into a bowl. Then he poured $\frac{1}{3}$ cup more flour into the bowl.

What is the total amount of flour Alan poured in the bowl?

Ⓐ $\frac{1}{3}$ cup

Ⓑ $\frac{2}{3}$ cup

Ⓒ $\frac{3}{3}$ cup

Ⓓ $\frac{1}{6}$ cup

4. Serena's frog hopped $\frac{2}{5}$ yard. Emily's frog hopped $\frac{3}{5}$ yard. How much farther did Emily's frog hop?

Ⓐ $\frac{1}{5}$ yard

Ⓑ $\frac{2}{5}$ yard

Ⓒ $\frac{3}{5}$ yard

Ⓓ $\frac{5}{5}$ yard

5. Gino studied $\frac{3}{4}$ hour for his test on Monday. He studied another $\frac{2}{4}$ hour on Tuesday. How long did he study in all?

Ⓐ $\frac{1}{4}$ hour

Ⓑ $\frac{3}{8}$ hour

Ⓒ $\frac{5}{8}$ hour

Ⓓ $1\frac{1}{4}$ hours

6. Allegra has a ribbon that is $\frac{9}{10}$ meter long. She cuts $\frac{5}{10}$ meter off of the ribbon. How long is the ribbon now?

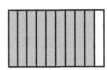

Ⓐ $\frac{4}{20}$ meter

Ⓑ $\frac{2}{10}$ meter

Ⓒ $\frac{2}{5}$ meter

Ⓓ $1\frac{4}{10}$ meters

Study the model. It is a good example of a written answer.

Student Model

Show

Kendra ran $\frac{7}{12}$ mile. Ryan ran $\frac{5}{12}$ mile. How much farther did Kendra run?

Use pictures, words, or numbers to show your work.

Subtract. $\frac{7}{12} - \frac{5}{12} = \frac{2}{12}$

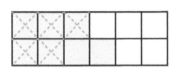

☑ The student shows each step.

Simplify. $\frac{2 \div 2}{12 \div 2} = \frac{1}{6}$

Explain

Solution: Kendra ran ____$\frac{1}{6}$____ mile farther than Ryan.

☑ The student correctly answers the question asked.

Explain how you got your answer.

I needed to subtract $\frac{7}{12} - \frac{5}{12}$. First, I drew a model of the problem. Then, I wrote a subtraction sentence.

I subtracted the numerators: $7 - 5 = 2$. I kept the same denominator. The difference is $\frac{2}{12}$. I simplified $\frac{2}{12}$ by dividing the numerator and denominator by their greatest common factor (GCF) 2, to get $\frac{1}{6}$.

☑ The student gives important details about how to find the difference.

☑ The student uses the math words *subtract*, *simplify*, *numerator*, and *denominator*.

Solve the problem. Use what you learned from the model.

CHECKLIST

Did you . . .

☐ show each step?

☐ answer the question asked?

☐ give important details?

☐ use math words?

7. Monica used $\frac{8}{10}$ gallon of paint for one room. She used $\frac{2}{10}$ gallon of paint for another room. How much paint did she use in all?

Use pictures, words, or numbers to show your work.

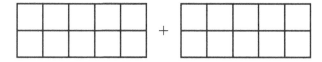

Solution: Monica used _____ gallon of paint in all.

Explain how you got your answer.

_____

_____

_____

_____

_____

As you add and subtract fractions, remember to
- draw models to represent the problem.
- use the greatest common factor (GCF) of the numerator and the denominator to simplify your fraction answers.

Solve each problem.

8. Mrs. Ramirez poured $\frac{1}{4}$ gallon cranberry juice into a pitcher. She also poured $\frac{2}{4}$ gallon orange juice in the pitcher. How many gallons of juice did she pour in the pitcher?

    Ⓐ $\frac{1}{4}$ gallon

    Ⓑ $\frac{1}{2}$ gallon

    Ⓒ $\frac{3}{4}$ gallon

    Ⓓ $\frac{4}{4}$ gallon

9. A bakery had $\frac{7}{9}$ of an apple pie and $\frac{3}{9}$ of a cherry pie. How much pie did the bakery have in all?

    Ⓐ $1\frac{1}{9}$

    Ⓑ $\frac{5}{9}$

    Ⓒ $\frac{4}{9}$

    Ⓓ $\frac{1}{9}$

10. Sue noticed that $\frac{6}{10}$ of the windows in an old building were broken. Then a bad storm broke another $\frac{2}{10}$ of the windows.

    What fraction of the windows are broken now?

    Ⓐ $\frac{2}{5}$

    Ⓑ $\frac{3}{5}$

    Ⓒ $\frac{4}{5}$

    Ⓓ $\frac{5}{5}$

11. Zeshon practiced piano for $\frac{3}{12}$ hour. He needs to practice for $\frac{9}{12}$ hour. How much longer does he need to practice?

    Ⓐ $\frac{1}{12}$ hour

    Ⓑ $\frac{1}{4}$ hour

    Ⓒ $\frac{1}{3}$ hour

    Ⓓ $\frac{1}{2}$ hour

12. Lena bought colorful beads to make bracelets for her jewelry store. She bought $\frac{5}{8}$ pound of purple beads and $\frac{7}{8}$ pound of silver beads. How many pounds of beads did she buy?

Ⓐ $\frac{1}{4}$ pound   Ⓒ $1\frac{1}{2}$ pound

Ⓑ $\frac{3}{4}$ pound   Ⓓ $1\frac{5}{8}$ pound

13. Vincent read $\frac{3}{5}$ of his book. He wants to read the entire book by tomorrow. What fraction of the book does he have left to read?

Ⓐ $\frac{1}{5}$ Ⓒ $\frac{3}{5}$

Ⓑ $\frac{2}{5}$ Ⓓ $\frac{5}{5}$

14. Jeslyn has $\frac{2}{3}$ yard of rope, Maria has $\frac{1}{3}$ yard of rope, and Maddie has $\frac{1}{3}$ yd of rope. They attach their ropes together end to end.

Write an expression to show the total length of the ropes. Then solve and simplify your answer.

Addition expression:

_____

Solution:

_____

_____ yards

15. Anna bought $\frac{9}{16}$ pound of grapes. She ate $\frac{5}{16}$ pound. How much does she have left? Use pictures, words, or numbers to show your work.

Solution: _____ pound

Explain how you found your answer.

_____

_____

_____

_____

 **How can you find common denominators for two unlike fractions?**

Explore

A **fraction** shows a part of a whole.

Like fractions have the same denominator.

Unlike fractions have different denominators.

like	unlike
$\frac{1}{3}$ and $\frac{2}{3}$	$\frac{2}{3}$ and $\frac{2}{5}$

You can always find a **common denominator** for unlike fractions.

How can you rewrite $\frac{2}{3}$ and $\frac{2}{5}$ with common denominators using a model?

Think

Make a model for each fraction.

To model $\frac{2}{3}$, divide a rectangle into __3__ equal parts and shade __2__ parts.

To model $\frac{2}{5}$, divide a rectangle into __5__ equal parts and shade __2__ parts.

Connect

To find a common denominator, you can find the **least common multiple (LCM)** of the denominators 3 and 5. Find the least number that has both 3 *and* 5 as factors.

List the multiples of each until you see a common multiple:

Multiples of 3: 3, 6, 9, 12, 15   Multiples of 5: 5, 10, 15, 20, 25

The LCM of 3 and 5 is 15. Adjust the models so they each have 15 equal parts.

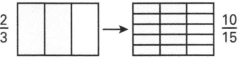

$\frac{2}{3}$ → $\frac{10}{15}$ Each of the 3 parts was divided into 5 parts. 10 parts are shaded.

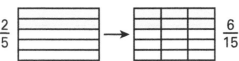

$\frac{2}{5}$ → $\frac{6}{15}$ Each of the 5 parts was divided into 3 parts. 6 parts are shaded.

Using the common denominator, the fractions can be written as $\frac{10}{15}$ and $\frac{6}{15}$.

Let's Talk

When $\frac{2}{3}$ was rewritten as $\frac{10}{15}$, how did the value change? Explain.

Fill in the blanks. Solve the problem.

Two friends keep their markers in identical boxes.
Alex's markers fill $\frac{1}{3}$ of the box, and Jarvis's markers fill $\frac{3}{4}$ of the box.
Rewrite these fractions using a common denominator.

■ To model $\frac{1}{3}$, divide a rectangle into _____ equal parts and shade _____ part.

To model $\frac{3}{4}$, divide a rectangle into _____ equal parts and shade _____ parts.

■ List the multiples of each until you see a common multiple:

Multiples of 3: ___, ___, ___, ___   Multiples of 4: ___, ___, ___, ___

The LCM of 3 and 4 is _____. This is the new denominator.

■ Adjust the model. Then rewrite the fractions.

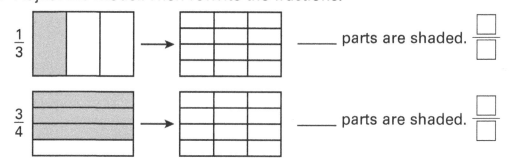

$\frac{1}{3}$ → _____ parts are shaded. $\frac{\square}{\square}$

$\frac{3}{4}$ → _____ parts are shaded. $\frac{\square}{\square}$

> To find the multiples of a number, multiply the number by 1, then 2, then 3, and so on.

Solution: Alex's markers fill _____ box, and Jarvis's markers fill _____ box.

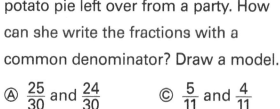 **Your Turn**   **Now, use what you know to solve this problem.**

1. Hannah has $\frac{5}{6}$ spinach pie and $\frac{4}{5}$ sweet potato pie left over from a party. How can she write the fractions with a common denominator? Draw a model.

Ⓐ $\frac{25}{30}$ and $\frac{24}{30}$ Ⓒ $\frac{5}{11}$ and $\frac{4}{11}$

Ⓑ $\frac{15}{18}$ and $\frac{12}{15}$ Ⓓ $\frac{5}{30}$ and $\frac{14}{30}$

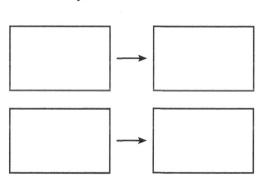

How can you compare fractions with different denominators?

Explore

Unlike fractions have different denominators. For example, $\frac{3}{8}$ and $\frac{4}{10}$ are unlike fractions.

Suppose Min ate $\frac{3}{8}$ of a sandwich and Carlos ate $\frac{4}{10}$ of a sandwich. How can you determine who ate more?

Think

Rewrite the fractions $\frac{3}{8}$ and $\frac{4}{10}$ using a common denominator.

The two denominators are __8__ and __10__.

Find the least common multiple of __8__ and __10__.

  Multiples of 8: 8, 16, __24__, __32__, __40__

  Multiples of 10: 10, 20, __30__, __40__, __50__

The LCM of 8 and 10 is __40__.

Connect

Rewrite $\frac{3}{8}$ using 40 as the denominator. Think, "8 multiplied by what number equals 40?" $8 \times 5 = 40$, so multiply both numerator and denominator of $\frac{3}{8}$ by 5.

$$\frac{3 \times 5}{8 \times 5} = \frac{15}{40}$$

Rewrite $\frac{4}{10}$ using 40 as the denominator. Think, "10 multiplied by what number equals 40?" $10 \times 4 = 40$, so multiply both numerator and denominator of $\frac{4}{10}$ by 4.

$$\frac{4 \times 4}{10 \times 4} = \frac{16}{40}$$

The denominators are now the same.
Compare the numerators to find which fraction is greater.

$15 < 16$, so $\frac{15}{40} < \frac{16}{40}$. Carlos ate more.

Let's Talk

Why should you rewrite unlike fractions with a common denominator to compare them?

Fill in the blanks. Solve the problem.

Jacob ran $\frac{7}{9}$ mile. Kelsey ran $\frac{5}{6}$ mile. Who ran farther?

■ Rewrite the two fractions using a common denominator.
The two denominators are _____ and _____.

■ Find the least common multiple of _____ and _____.
Multiples of 9: _____, _____ , _____
Multiples of 6: _____, _____, _____
The LCM of 9 and 6 is _____. This is the new denominator.

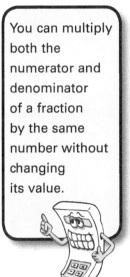

You can multiply both the numerator and denominator of a fraction by the same number without changing its value.

■ Rewrite $\frac{7}{9}$ using 18 as the denominator.
$9 \times 2 = 18$, so multiply both numerator and denominator
of $\frac{7}{9}$ by _____.

$$\frac{7 \times \boxed{}}{9 \times \boxed{}} = \frac{\boxed{}}{\boxed{}}$$

■ Rewrite $\frac{5}{6}$ using 18 as the denominator.
$6 \times 3 = 18$, so multiply both numerator and denominator
of $\frac{5}{6}$ by _____.

$$\frac{5 \times \boxed{}}{6 \times \boxed{}} = \frac{\boxed{}}{\boxed{}}$$

■ Compare the numerators: $14 < 15$, so $\frac{14}{18}$ _____ $\frac{15}{18}$.

Solution: _____ ran farther than _____.

Your Turn

Now, use what you know to solve this problem.

2. Xia bought $\frac{2}{3}$ pound of green apples. Ryan bought
$\frac{5}{8}$ pound of red apples. Write $<$, $>$, or $=$ to show
if Xia bought less, more, or the same amount of
apples as Ryan.

$$\frac{2}{3} \underline{} \frac{5}{8}$$

_____ bought more apples than _____.

Solve the problem. Then read why each answer choice is correct or not correct.

Solve

Tia picked $\frac{2}{10}$ pound of strawberries. Tyrone picked $\frac{1}{4}$ pound of strawberries. Which number sentence correctly compares the amounts of strawberries they picked?

Ⓐ $\frac{4}{20} > \frac{1}{4}$

Ⓑ $\frac{4}{20} > \frac{4}{16}$

Ⓒ $\frac{4}{20} < \frac{5}{20}$

Ⓓ $\frac{4}{20} = \frac{4}{20}$

Check

Check to see if you chose the correct answer.

Find the least common multiple to rewrite $\frac{2}{10}$ and $\frac{1}{4}$ with a common denominator.

Multiples of 10: 10, **20**, 30, 40, 50   Multiples of 4: 4, 8, 12, 16, **20**

The LCM is 20. Rewrite the fractions using 20 as the common denominator.

$\frac{2 \times 2}{10 \times 2} = \frac{4}{20}$ and $\frac{1 \times 5}{4 \times 5} = \frac{5}{20}$

Compare. $4 < 5$, so $\frac{4}{20} < \frac{5}{20}$.

So, the correct answer is Ⓒ.

Why are the other answer choices not correct?

Ⓐ $\frac{4}{20} > \frac{1}{4}$	Rewrite *both* fractions with a common denominator. Then compare the numerators.
Ⓑ $\frac{4}{20} > \frac{4}{16}$	Rewrite so there is a common denominator, not a common numerator.
Ⓓ $\frac{4}{20} = \frac{4}{20}$	$\frac{1}{4}$ rewritten with a denominator of 20 is $\frac{5}{20}$, not $\frac{4}{20}$.

Your Turn ➤ Solve each problem. Use the hints to avoid mistakes.

- To compare fractions, first use the least common multiple (LCM) of the denominators to rewrite the fractions with a common denominator.
- Then use the numerators of the like fractions to make a comparison.
- Be sure to check your calculations when writing equivalent fractions.

3. Several students compared fractions. They wrote these number sentences on the board. Which of these number sentences is true?

   Ⓐ $\frac{2}{7} > \frac{5}{9}$

   Ⓑ $\frac{3}{5} < \frac{5}{8}$

   Ⓒ $\frac{1}{2} > \frac{4}{8}$

   Ⓓ $\frac{4}{5} < \frac{4}{10}$

4. Which of these fractions is greater than $\frac{3}{5}$?

   Ⓐ $\frac{7}{15}$

   Ⓑ $\frac{2}{8}$

   Ⓒ $\frac{4}{10}$

   Ⓓ $\frac{3}{4}$

5. How can you rewrite $\frac{3}{8}$ and $\frac{5}{7}$ with a common denominator?

   Ⓐ $\frac{3}{8}$ and $\frac{6}{8}$

   Ⓑ $\frac{21}{56}$ and $\frac{40}{56}$

   Ⓒ $\frac{3}{15}$ and $\frac{5}{15}$

   Ⓓ $\frac{12}{32}$ and $\frac{20}{28}$

6. Four friends are reading the same book. Marcus has read $\frac{3}{4}$ of the book. Talia read $\frac{1}{2}$, Jonas read $\frac{11}{16}$, and Rita read $\frac{5}{8}$ of the book. Who has read the most?

   Ⓐ Marcus

   Ⓑ Talia

   Ⓒ Jonas

   Ⓓ Rita

Study the model. It is a good example of a written answer.

Student Model

Show

Myra bought $\frac{2}{3}$ yard of blue fabric and $\frac{5}{7}$ yard of red fabric. Which color did she buy more of?

Use pictures, words, or numbers to show your work.

Compare $\frac{2}{3}$ and $\frac{5}{7}$.

Find the LCM of 3 and 7.
Multiples of 3: 3, 6, 9, 12, 15, 18, (21)
Multiples of 7: 7, 14, (21), 28, 35, 42 } LCM = 21

✓ The student shows each step.

Rewrite the fractions.

$\frac{2 \times 7}{3 \times 7} = \frac{14}{21}$ and $\frac{5 \times 3}{7 \times 3} = \frac{15}{21}$

Compare. $14 < 15$, so $\frac{14}{21} < \frac{15}{21}$, and $\frac{2}{3} < \frac{5}{7}$.

✓ The student correctly answers the question asked.

Solution: Myra bought more __red__ fabric than __blue__ fabric.

Explain

Explain how you got your answer.

I needed to compare $\frac{2}{3}$ and $\frac{5}{7}$. They are unlike

fractions, so I found the LCM of the denominators.

✓ The student gives important details about how to find the answer.

Then, I rewrote the fractions using the LCM, 21,

as the common denominator. Finally, I compared the

numerators of the like fractions to find the answer.

✓ The student uses the math words *unlike fractions, LCM, common denominator,* and *like fractions.*

Because $\frac{2}{3} < \frac{5}{7}$, Myra bought more red fabric.

7. Tomás drank $\frac{5}{8}$ of a gallon of water. Seth drank $\frac{7}{12}$ of a gallon of water. Who drank more water?

Use pictures, words, or numbers to show your work.

> ☑ CHECKLIST
>
> Did you . . .
>
> ☐ show each step?
>
> ☐ answer the question asked?
>
> ☐ give important details?
>
> ☐ use math words?

Solution: _____ drank more water than _____.

Explain how you got your answer.

_____

_____

_____

_____

_____

As you solve fraction problems, remember to

• use models to help you compare fractions.

• list multiples of the denominators to find a common denominator.

• multiply both numerator and denominator by the same number when rewriting with a common denominator.

Solve each problem.

8. What common denominator can you use to rewrite $\frac{1}{6}$ and $\frac{3}{8}$ as like fractions?

Ⓐ 6

Ⓑ 8

Ⓒ 14

Ⓓ 24

9. The models show $\frac{1}{2}$ and $\frac{3}{7}$ rewritten as like fractions.

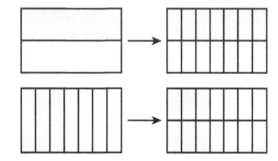

What are the like fractions?

Ⓐ $\frac{1}{9}$ and $\frac{3}{9}$

Ⓑ $\frac{7}{14}$ and $\frac{6}{14}$

Ⓒ $\frac{2}{7}$ and $\frac{7}{10}$

Ⓓ $\frac{7}{14}$ and $\frac{8}{14}$

10. Nakil rode his bike $\frac{2}{5}$ mile. Desiree walked $\frac{3}{4}$ mile. Which number sentence can you use to compare how far they went?

Ⓐ $\frac{8}{20} < \frac{15}{20}$

Ⓑ $\frac{2}{9} < \frac{3}{9}$

Ⓒ $\frac{5}{20} < \frac{8}{9}$

Ⓓ $\frac{2}{20} < \frac{3}{20}$

11. Which fraction is less than $\frac{4}{12}$?

Ⓐ $\frac{4}{10}$

Ⓑ $\frac{5}{6}$

Ⓒ $\frac{1}{4}$

Ⓓ $\frac{3}{8}$

12. Which number sentence is true?

Ⓐ $\frac{1}{4} > \frac{3}{5}$

Ⓑ $\frac{1}{2} < \frac{4}{5}$

Ⓒ $\frac{2}{9} > \frac{1}{2}$

Ⓓ $\frac{3}{4} < \frac{8}{11}$

13. Jennie's tomato plant grew $\frac{4}{9}$ foot. Her bamboo plant grew $\frac{7}{8}$ foot. Which number sentence correctly compares how much the plants grew?

Ⓐ $\frac{4}{9} < \frac{7}{8}$

Ⓑ $\frac{4}{9} = \frac{7}{8}$

Ⓒ $\frac{4}{9} > \frac{7}{8}$

Ⓓ $\frac{4}{9} + \frac{7}{8}$

14. Stefan is making a tree house. He has one board that is $\frac{7}{8}$ meter long. He has another board that is $\frac{3}{4}$ meter long. Rewrite the fractions with a common denominator. Then write a number sentence that compares the fractions.

Like fractions:

_____ and _____

Number sentence:

_____

15. Sarah made $\frac{3}{5}$ gallon of lemonade and $\frac{4}{9}$ gallon of fruit punch. Which drink did she make more of?

Use pictures, words, or numbers to show your work.

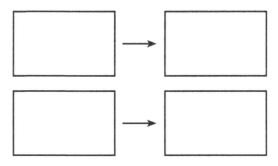

Solution: Sarah made more _____ than _____.

Explain how you found your answer.

_____

_____

_____

_____

_____

Lesson 10 ADD AND SUBTRACT UNLIKE FRACTIONS

PART ONE: Learn About Adding Unlike Fractions

 **How can you add fractions with different denominators?**

Explore

Like fractions have the same denominator. To add like fractions, you add the numerators and keep the same denominator. $\frac{3}{6} + \frac{2}{6} = \frac{5}{6}$

How can you find the sum of two **unlike fractions**? $\frac{1}{5} + \frac{4}{10}$

Think

Rewrite the unlike fractions using a **common denominator**. To find a common denominator, you can find the **least common multiple (LCM)** of the denominators 5 and 10.

Multiples of 5: __5__, __10__
Multiples of 10: __10__, __20__

The LCM of 5 and 10 is __10__.

The fraction $\frac{4}{10}$ already has a denominator of 10.

It does not need to be renamed.

Write $\frac{1}{5}$ with a denominator of 10.

$\frac{1 \times \boxed{2}}{5 \times \boxed{2}} = \frac{\boxed{2}}{\boxed{10}}$ So, $\frac{1}{5} = \frac{\boxed{2}}{\boxed{10}}$.

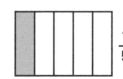

$\frac{4}{10}$

$\frac{1}{5} = \frac{2}{10}$

Connect

Rewrite the problem using the renamed fractions. $\frac{4}{10} + \frac{2}{10}$

Add the numerators and keep the same denominator. $\frac{4}{10} + \frac{2}{10} = \frac{6}{10}$

Simplify your answer. Divide the numerator and denominator by their **greatest common factor (GCF)**, 2.

$\frac{6 \div 2}{10 \div 2} = \frac{3}{5}$

Let's Talk

Is it true that multiplying the numerator and the denominator of **any** fraction by the same number does not change the value of the fraction? Give examples to explain your answer.

Fill in the blanks. Solve the problem.

Mike is baking two different types of cookies. One recipe calls for $\frac{1}{4}$ cup of flour. The other recipe needs $\frac{1}{2}$ cup of flour. How much flour does he need all together?

■ How can you find $\frac{1}{4} + \frac{1}{2}$?

■ What are some multiples of 2? _____, _____, _____

What are some multiples of 4? _____, _____, _____

What is the least common multiple of 2 and 4? _____

■ Which fraction does not need to be renamed? Shade the model.

> When you need to find the common denominator of two fractions, always check to see if the greater denominator is a multiple of the other denominator.

■ Write the other fraction with the common denominator. Shade the model to help you.

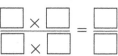  

■ Rewrite the problem using the fractions with the common denominator. Then add.

Solution: Mike needs _____ cup of flour to make the cookies.

Your Turn  **Now, use what you know to solve this problem.**

1. Gary combined $\frac{1}{6}$ pound of peanuts with $\frac{2}{5}$ pound of pretzels to make snack mix. How much snack mix did he make?

  Ⓐ $\frac{3}{6}$ lb   Ⓒ $\frac{3}{30}$ lb

  Ⓑ $\frac{17}{30}$ lb   Ⓓ $\frac{3}{11}$ lb

 **?** How can you subtract fractions with different denominators?

Explore

To find the difference of like fractions, you can subtract the numerators and keep the same denominator. $\frac{5}{6} - \frac{4}{6} = \frac{1}{6}$

How can you find the difference of two unlike fractions? $\frac{3}{4} - \frac{1}{3}$

Think

Rewrite the fractions using a common denominator. To find a common denominator, you can find the least common multiple (LCM) of the denominators 4 and 3.

Multiples of 4: __4__, __8__, __12__, __16__

Multiples of 3: __3__, __6__, __9__, __12__

The LCM of 4 and 3 is __12__.

Write each fraction with a denominator of 12.

$\frac{3 \times \boxed{3}}{4 \times \boxed{3}} = \frac{\boxed{9}}{\boxed{12}}$ and $\frac{1 \times \boxed{4}}{3 \times \boxed{4}} = \frac{\boxed{4}}{\boxed{12}}$

So, $\frac{3}{4} = \frac{\boxed{9}}{\boxed{12}}$ and $\frac{1}{3} = \frac{\boxed{4}}{\boxed{12}}$.

Connect

Rewrite the problem using the renamed fractions.

$\frac{9}{12} - \frac{4}{12}$

Subtract the numerators and keep the same denominator.

So, $\frac{9}{12} - \frac{4}{12} = \frac{5}{12}$.

The answer $\frac{5}{12}$ is in **simplest form**.

The crossed-out parts show $\frac{4}{12}$ subtracted from $\frac{9}{12}$, the shaded parts.

Let's Talk

When adding or subtracting fractions, when must you find a common denominator? Give two examples.

Think It Through

Fill in the blanks. Solve the problem.

Tina has $\frac{5}{8}$ of a birthday cake. She and her brother eat $\frac{1}{3}$ of the cake. How much of the cake is left?

- How can you find $\frac{5}{8} - \frac{1}{3}$?

- What are some multiples of 8? _____, _____, _____, _____

  What are some multiples of 3? _____, _____, _____, _____, _____, _____, _____, _____

  What is the least common multiple of 3 and 8? _____

- Write each fraction with the common denominator.

  $\dfrac{5 \times \square}{8 \times \square} = \dfrac{\square}{\square}$ and $\dfrac{1 \times \square}{3 \times \square} = \dfrac{\square}{\square}$

- Rewrite the problem using the like fractions. Then subtract. Use the model to help you.

  $\dfrac{\square}{\square} - \dfrac{\square}{\square} = \dfrac{\square}{\square}$

Solution: There is _____ of the cake left.

> Sometimes you have to find many multiples before reaching a common multiple.

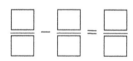 Now, use what you know to solve this problem.

2. Rachel is walking to her friend's house, which is $\frac{7}{8}$ mile away. She has already walked $\frac{3}{4}$ mile. How much farther does she have to walk?

   Simplify your answer.

   $\dfrac{7}{8} - \dfrac{3}{4} = $ _____ mile

Solve the problem. Then read why each answer choice is correct or not correct.

Solve

On Monday, Lamar ran for $\frac{1}{3}$ of an hour. On Tuesday, he ran for $\frac{2}{5}$ of an hour. How long did Lamar run in all?

Ⓐ $\frac{3}{8}$ hour

Ⓑ $\frac{11}{15}$ hour

Ⓒ $\frac{3}{15}$ hour

Ⓓ $\frac{7}{15}$ hour

Check

Check to see if you chose the correct answer.

To find the sum, rewrite the fractions using a common denominator. The LCM of 3 and 5 is 15.

$$\frac{1 \times 5}{3 \times 5} = \frac{5}{15} \text{ and } \frac{2 \times 3}{5 \times 3} = \frac{6}{15}$$

Add the like fractions.

$$\frac{5}{15} + \frac{6}{15} = \frac{11}{15}$$

So, the correct answer is Ⓑ.

Why are the other answer choices not correct?

Ⓐ $\frac{3}{8}$ hour	To add two unlike fractions, you need to first rewrite the fractions with a common denominator. You can't just add the numerators and the denominators.
Ⓒ $\frac{3}{15}$ hour	When rewriting fractions with a common denominator, be sure to rewrite the numerators as well.
Ⓓ $\frac{7}{15}$ hour	Remember to rewrite the numerators of *both* fractions.

> • Before adding or subtracting, rewrite unlike fractions using the least common multiple (LCM) of the denominators as the common denominator.
> • To add like fractions, add the numerators and keep the common denominator.
> • To subtract like fractions, subtract the numerators and keep the common denominator.

3. For the addition problem below, what is the LCM that can be used for the common denominator?

$$\frac{1}{6} + \frac{3}{4}$$

Ⓐ 4

Ⓑ 10

Ⓒ 12

Ⓓ 24

4. Which fraction shows $\frac{2}{7}$ rewritten with a denominator of 28?

Ⓐ $\frac{28}{98}$

Ⓑ $\frac{8}{28}$

Ⓒ $\frac{2}{28}$

Ⓓ $\frac{1}{28}$

5. Trish bought tickets to use at the county fair. She used $\frac{2}{3}$ of her tickets for rides and $\frac{1}{7}$ of the tickets for food. What fraction shows the difference:

$\frac{2}{3} - \frac{1}{7}$?

Ⓐ $\frac{1}{4}$

Ⓑ $\frac{6}{14}$

Ⓒ $\frac{1}{21}$

Ⓓ $\frac{11}{21}$

6. Sam is helping his dad fill a sandbox with new sand. They fill $\frac{1}{5}$ before lunch and $\frac{1}{2}$ after lunch. How much of the box is filled with new sand?

Ⓐ $\frac{2}{7}$

Ⓑ $\frac{7}{10}$

Ⓒ $\frac{2}{10}$

Ⓓ $\frac{2}{5}$

Study the model. It is a good example of a written answer.

Student Model

Show

Andrew is reading a book for his book club. He read $\frac{1}{6}$ of the book on Tuesday and $\frac{1}{3}$ of the book on Wednesday. What fraction of the book has Andrew read so far?

Use pictures, words, or numbers to show your work.

Add. $\frac{1}{6} + \frac{1}{3}$

Find the LCM of 3 and 6.

Multiples of 3: 3, ⑥, 9

Multiples of 6: ⑥, 12, 18 $\Big\}$ LCM = 6

☑ The student shows each step.

Rename $\frac{1}{3}$ and add.

$\frac{1}{3} = \frac{1 \times 2}{3 \times 2} = \frac{2}{6}$ $\frac{1}{6} + \frac{2}{6} = \frac{3}{6}$

Simplify. $\frac{3 \div 3}{6 \div 3} = \frac{1}{2}$

Solution: Andrew has read $\frac{1}{2}$ of the book.

☑ The student correctly answers the question asked.

Explain

Explain how you got your answer.

First, I wrote the addition problem. Next, I wanted to rewrite each fraction so that they have a common denominator equal to the LCM. So, I found the LCM of 3 and 6, which is 6. The fraction $\frac{1}{6}$ already has a denominator of 6, so I only rewrote the second fraction, $\frac{1}{3}$, as $\frac{2}{6}$. Then, I added the two like fractions. Finally, I simplified my answer.

☑ The student gives important details about how to find the answer.

☑ The student uses the math words *LCM*, *common denominator*, and *simplify*.

7. Mrs. Henderson had $\frac{7}{12}$ dozen eggs in her refrigerator. Then she used $\frac{1}{6}$ dozen eggs to make a cake. What fraction of a dozen is left?

Use pictures, words, or numbers to show your work.

☑ CHECKLIST

Did you . . .

☐ show each step?

☐ answer the question asked?

☐ give important details?

☐ use math words?

Solution: There are _____ dozen eggs left.

Explain how you got your answer.

_____

_____

_____

_____

_____

As you solve fraction problems involving addition or subtraction, remember to

- find the least common multiple (LCM) to rewrite fractions with a common denominator.
- use models to show the fractions and help you add or subtract.
- simplify answers by dividing the numerator and denominator by their greatest common factor (GCF), as needed.

Solve each problem.

8. One-fifth of Mr. Johnson's class had their class pictures taken this morning. One-third of the class had them taken this afternoon. What fraction of the class had their class picture taken today?

   Ⓐ $\frac{2}{15}$

   Ⓑ $\frac{1}{4}$

   Ⓒ $\frac{2}{8}$

   Ⓓ $\frac{8}{15}$

9. Which model shows $\frac{3}{4} - \frac{7}{12}$?

   Ⓐ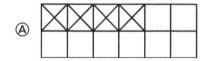

   Ⓑ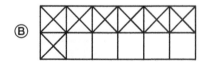

   Ⓒ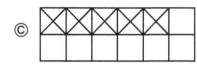

   Ⓓ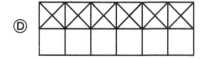

10. Of the graphic novels on a rack, $\frac{1}{6}$ are mysteries and $\frac{1}{4}$ are science fiction. What fraction represents the graphic novels on the rack that are mystery or science fiction?

    Ⓐ $\frac{1}{10}$

    Ⓑ $\frac{5}{12}$

    Ⓒ $\frac{2}{10}$

    Ⓓ $\frac{10}{24}$

11. Peter is finding $\frac{2}{3} - \frac{2}{7}$. What is the common denominator and the difference?

    Ⓐ 3, $\frac{5}{12}$

    Ⓑ 21, $\frac{4}{21}$

    Ⓒ 21, $\frac{8}{21}$

    Ⓓ 10, $\frac{0}{10}$

12. What is $\frac{3}{8}$ more than $\frac{1}{16}$?

(A) $\frac{1}{6}$ (C) $\frac{7}{16}$

(B) $\frac{5}{16}$ (D) $\frac{1}{8}$

13. What number belongs in the box?

$$\frac{7}{9} - \frac{1}{4} = \blacksquare$$

(A) $\frac{19}{36}$ (C) $\frac{6}{5}$

(B) $\frac{6}{9}$ (D) $\frac{6}{36}$

14. Nathan is trying to find $\frac{2}{5} + \frac{3}{7}$. List multiples to help him find a common denominator.

Multiples of 5:

_____

Multiples of 7:

_____

Least common multiple of 5 and 7: _____

Common denominator: _____

15. A cake recipe calls for $\frac{2}{3}$ cup of sugar. If Donna has already added $\frac{1}{2}$ cup, how much more does she need?

Use pictures, words, or numbers to show your work.

Solution: Donna still needs to add _____ cup of sugar.

Explain how you found your answer.

_____

_____

_____

_____

_____

How can you add mixed numbers?

Mixed numbers have a whole number and a fraction. They can also be written as **improper fractions**, which have a numerator that is greater than or equal to the denominator.

$1\frac{2}{3}$ ▢▢▢ $\frac{5}{3}$ ▢▢▢▢

How can you add mixed numbers?

$5\frac{2}{5} + 2\frac{4}{5}$

$5\frac{2}{5}$ means __5__ wholes plus __$\frac{2}{5}$__, and $2\frac{4}{5}$ means __2__ wholes plus __$\frac{4}{5}$__.

Shade the models to show the amounts.

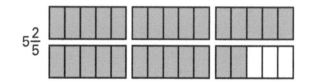

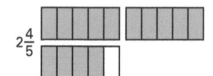

Set up the problem. Add the fractions first. Then add the whole numbers. If needed, simplify the answer.

The sum is $7\frac{6}{5}$.

Rename $7\frac{6}{5}$ so it's a mixed number with a proper fraction.

$8\frac{1}{5}$ is in **simplest form**.

$$\begin{array}{r} 5\frac{2}{5} \\ + 2\frac{4}{5} \\ \hline 7\frac{6}{5} \end{array}$$

$$7\frac{6}{5} = 7 + \frac{5}{5} + \frac{1}{5} = 8\frac{1}{5}$$

Let's Talk Explain how to rename $4\frac{7}{4}$ as $5\frac{3}{4}$.

Fill in the blanks. Solve the problem.

Angelica mixed $2\frac{3}{4}$ cups fruit juice with $4\frac{3}{4}$ cups water to make punch.

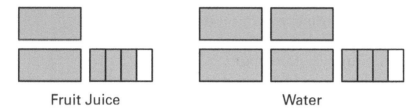

Fruit Juice   Water

How many cups of punch did Angelica make in all?

Because $2\frac{3}{4}$ is about 3, and $4\frac{3}{4}$ is about 5, the sum should be about $3 + 5 = 8$.

■ Set up the problem.

  Add the fractions first.

  Then add the whole numbers.

$$2\frac{3}{4}$$
$$+\ 4\frac{3}{4}$$
$$\overline{\square\frac{\square}{\square}}$$

■ Rename the sum. $\square\frac{\square}{\square} = 6 + \frac{\square}{\square} + \frac{2}{4} = \square\frac{\square}{\square}$

■ **Simplify** the fraction. $\frac{2 \div 2}{4 \div 2} = \frac{\square}{\square}$ So, $\square\frac{\square}{\square} = \square\frac{\square}{\square}$.

Solution: Angelica made _____ cups of punch.

Your Turn   **Now, use what you know to solve this problem.**

1. Daniel's bamboo plant grew $4\frac{3}{8}$ inches in the first week. It grew $5\frac{7}{8}$ inches in the second week. What is the total amount it grew during the two weeks? Remember to simplify.

  Ⓐ $\frac{10}{8}$ inches   Ⓒ $9\frac{1}{2}$ inches

  Ⓑ $9\frac{1}{4}$ inches   Ⓓ $10\frac{1}{4}$ inches

? How can you subtract mixed numbers?

Explore

Like fractions have the same denominator.
Unlike fractions have different denominators.
To subtract unlike fractions, rewrite the fractions
using a **common denominator**. Then subtract
the numerators. Simplify if needed.

$$\frac{4}{5} - \frac{1}{3}$$

$$\frac{4}{5} \underset{\times 3}{\overset{\times 3}{=}} \frac{12}{15} \qquad \frac{1}{3} \underset{\times 5}{\overset{\times 5}{=}} \frac{5}{15}$$

$$\frac{12}{15} - \frac{5}{15} = \frac{7}{15}$$

How can you subtract mixed numbers?

$$4\frac{1}{8} - 1\frac{5}{12}$$

Think

Find a common denominator by finding the **least common
multiple (LCM)** of the denominators.

Multiples of 8: 8, __16__, __24__   Multiples of 12: 12, __24__

The LCM of 8 and 12 is __24__.

Rewrite the fractions using the common denominator. The whole
numbers stay the same.

$$4\frac{1}{8} = 4\frac{\boxed{3}}{24} \qquad \text{and} \qquad 1\frac{5}{12} = 1\frac{\boxed{10}}{24}$$

Connect

Rewrite the problem. $4\frac{3}{24} - 1\frac{10}{24}$

If needed, rename the fraction to be subtracted.

Because $\frac{3}{24} < \frac{10}{24}$, rename $4\frac{3}{24}$.

Regroup 1 whole as $\frac{24}{24}$ and add $\frac{24}{24}$ to $\frac{3}{24}$. $4\frac{3}{24} = 3 + \frac{24}{24} + \frac{3}{24} = 3\frac{27}{24}$

Subtract the fractions, and then subtract the whole numbers.

$$3\frac{27}{24} - 1\frac{10}{24} = 2\frac{17}{24}$$

Let's Talk

Explain when you would *not* need to rename a mixed number before
subtracting. Give an example.

Fill in the blanks. Solve the problem.

Raj has $5\frac{1}{6}$ feet of border for his room. He cut off a piece that was $2\frac{2}{3}$ feet long. What is the length of the border Raj has left?

■ Find a common denominator. What is the LCM of 6 and 3?

Multiples of 6: 6, _____   Multiples of 3: 3, _____

The LCM of 6 and 3 is _____.

■ Rewrite the fractions using the common denominator as needed.

The fraction _____already has the common denominator.

It _____ need to be rewritten.

$2\frac{2}{3} = 2\frac{\square}{\square}$

■ Rewrite the problem. $5\frac{1}{6} - 2\frac{\square}{\square}$

$\frac{1}{6} < \frac{4}{6}$, so rename $5\frac{1}{6}$. $5\frac{1}{6} = 4 + \frac{\square}{\square} + \frac{1}{6} = 4\frac{\square}{6}$

■ Rewrite the problem again.
Subtract the fractions. Then subtract whole numbers. Simplify.

$4\frac{\square}{\square} - \square\frac{\square}{\square} = \square\frac{\square}{\square} = \square\frac{\square}{\square}$

Solution: Raj has _____ feet of border left.

> Once you rewrite the fractions, compare the numerators.
>
> Rename if the numerator being subtracted is greater than the numerator from which you are subtracting.

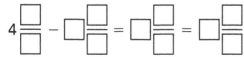 **Now, use what you know to solve this problem.**

2. Kathryn walked $3\frac{5}{6}$ miles on Saturday. She walked $2\frac{3}{4}$ miles on Sunday. How much farther did she walk on Saturday? Show your work.

_____ miles

Solve the problem. Then read why each answer choice is correct or not correct.

Solve

Mrs. Sanchez bought $2\frac{3}{4}$ pounds of grapes and $3\frac{1}{2}$ pounds of strawberries. How much fruit did she buy in all?

Ⓐ $5\frac{5}{8}$ lb

Ⓑ $5\frac{4}{5}$ lb

Ⓒ $6\frac{1}{4}$ lb

Ⓓ $6\frac{5}{4}$ lb

Check

Check to see if you chose the correct answer.

Add $2\frac{3}{4} + 3\frac{1}{2}$.

Rewrite the fractions with a common denominator. $2\frac{3}{4}$ and $3\frac{2}{4}$

Add the fractions first. Then add the whole numbers. $2\frac{3}{4} + 3\frac{2}{4} = 5\frac{5}{4}$

Rename the sum so it's a mixed number with a proper fraction.

$5\frac{5}{4} = 5 + \frac{4}{4} + \frac{1}{4} = 6\frac{1}{4}$

So, the correct answer is Ⓒ.

Why are the other answer choices not correct?

Ⓐ $5\frac{5}{8}$ lb	After finding a common denominator, only the numerators should be added.
Ⓑ $5\frac{4}{5}$ lb	$5\frac{5}{4}$ was renamed by finding the reciprocal of the fraction. To rename $5\frac{5}{4}$, find $5 + \frac{5}{4}$, or $5 + \frac{4}{4} + \frac{1}{4}$.
Ⓓ $6\frac{5}{4}$ lb	When renaming $5\frac{5}{4}$ by increasing the whole number by 1 whole, you also need to decrease the fraction by 1 whole.

- Decide whether you need to add or subtract.
- Check if the fractions have a common denominator. If not, use the least common multiple (LCM) of the denominators to rewrite the fractions with a common denominator.
- Rename and simplify as needed so the answer is a mixed number with a fraction in simplest form.

3. Oscar finished his book in two days. He read for $1\frac{5}{6}$ hours on Tuesday and $1\frac{1}{3}$ hours on Wednesday. How long did it take for Oscar to finish his book?

    Ⓐ $\frac{1}{6}$ hour

    Ⓑ $2\frac{1}{6}$ hours

    Ⓒ $2\frac{2}{3}$ hours

    Ⓓ $3\frac{1}{6}$ hours

4. A large bottle of perfume contains $3\frac{5}{8}$ ounces. A small bottle contains $2\frac{1}{3}$ ounces. How many more ounces does the large bottle contain?

    Ⓐ $\frac{7}{24}$ oz

    Ⓑ $1\frac{1}{6}$ oz

    Ⓒ $1\frac{7}{24}$ oz

    Ⓓ $1\frac{4}{5}$ oz

5. Cassia is making two kinds of cookies. She needs $2\frac{4}{5}$ cups of sugar for one recipe. She needs $1\frac{2}{5}$ cups of sugar for the other. How much sugar does she need in all?

    Ⓐ $\frac{1}{5}$ cup

    Ⓑ $1\frac{2}{5}$ cups

    Ⓒ $3\frac{3}{5}$ cups

    Ⓓ $4\frac{1}{5}$ cups

6. Jacob's garden is $8\frac{5}{10}$ meters long and $6\frac{4}{5}$ meters wide. How much longer is the garden than it is wide?

    Ⓐ $1\frac{7}{10}$ m

    Ⓑ $2\frac{1}{5}$ m

    Ⓒ $2\frac{3}{10}$ m

    Ⓓ $15\frac{3}{10}$ m

Study the model. It is a good example of a written answer.

Student Model

Show

Ken rides his scooter from *A* to *B*. He takes a break, and then he rides from *B* to *C*. How far does Ken ride in all?

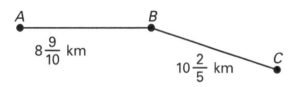

A _____ B

$8\frac{9}{10}$ km

$10\frac{2}{5}$ km C

Use pictures, words, or numbers to show your work.

The LCM of 5 and 10 is 10. $8\frac{9}{10}$ and $10\frac{2}{5} = 10\frac{4}{10}$

☑ The student shows each step.

Add. $8\frac{9}{10}$

$+ 10\frac{4}{10}$
_____
$18\frac{13}{10}$

Rename.

$18\frac{13}{10} = 18 + \frac{10}{10} + \frac{3}{10} = 19\frac{3}{10}$

☑ The student correctly answers the question asked.

Solution: Ken rides $\underline{19\frac{3}{10}}$ km in all.

Explain

Explain how you got your answer.

I needed to add two mixed numbers $8\frac{9}{10}$ and $10\frac{2}{5}$. They

had unlike denominators, so I used the LCM to rewrite

$10\frac{2}{5}$ with the common denominator, 10. I added the

fractions, then the whole numbers. My answer was a

mixed number with an improper fraction, so I renamed

it as a mixed number with a proper fraction.

☑ The student gives important details about how to find the total.

☑ The student uses the math words *mixed numbers, unlike denominators, LCM,* and *common denominator.*

7. Helene needs $4\frac{2}{3}$ yards of fabric to make a tablecloth.
   She needs another $3\frac{1}{2}$ yards of fabric to make napkins.
   How much fabric does she need in all?
   Use pictures, words, or numbers to show your work.

☑ CHECKLIST

Did you . . .

☐ show each step?

☐ answer the question asked?

☐ give important details?

☐ use math words?

Solution: Helene needs _____ yards of fabric in all.

Explain how you got your answer.

_____

_____

_____

_____

As you solve mixed-number problems, remember to
- use the least common multiple (LCM) of the denominators to rename unlike fractions before adding or subtracting them.
- rename any mixed-number answers that have improper fractions.

Solve each problem.

8. Samuel's puppy weighs $12\frac{7}{8}$ pounds. Last month, it weighed $8\frac{3}{8}$ pounds. How much weight did the puppy gain?

   Ⓐ $21\frac{1}{4}$ lb

   Ⓑ 8 lb

   Ⓒ $5\frac{1}{4}$ lb

   Ⓓ $4\frac{1}{2}$ lb

9. Which expression has a sum of $6\frac{1}{6}$?

   Ⓐ $2\frac{5}{6} + 3\frac{1}{3}$

   Ⓑ $3\frac{1}{6} + 3\frac{1}{6}$

   Ⓒ $4\frac{1}{2} + 2\frac{1}{4}$

   Ⓓ $1\frac{1}{12} + 5\frac{5}{6}$

10. Kendra's town received $9\frac{5}{8}$ inches of rain during the first half of the year. It received $6\frac{2}{3}$ inches of rain during the second half of the year. How much rain did Kendra's town receive in all?

    Ⓐ $15\frac{7}{11}$ in.

    Ⓑ $15\frac{7}{8}$ in.

    Ⓒ $16\frac{7}{24}$ in.

    Ⓓ $22\frac{1}{11}$ in.

11. McKenna is $4\frac{1}{4}$ feet tall. Her younger brother is $2\frac{4}{6}$ feet tall. How much taller is McKenna?

    Ⓐ $1\frac{1}{3}$ ft

    Ⓑ $1\frac{7}{12}$ ft

    Ⓒ $2\frac{5}{12}$ ft

    Ⓓ $6\frac{11}{12}$ ft

12. The Perez family rode on a train for $3\frac{2}{3}$ hours. Then they drove for $2\frac{1}{4}$ hours. How many hours did they travel in all?

Ⓐ $5\frac{3}{7}$ hours

Ⓒ $5\frac{11}{12}$ hours

Ⓑ $5\frac{11}{24}$ hours

Ⓓ $6\frac{1}{12}$ hours

13. Kayla's hair was $12\frac{3}{5}$ inches long. Yesterday, she had $2\frac{1}{3}$ inches cut off. How long is her hair now?

Ⓐ $10\frac{4}{15}$ in.

Ⓒ $10\frac{9}{5}$ in.

Ⓑ $10\frac{4}{5}$ in.

Ⓓ 11 in.

14. Desiree is using the recipe below.

Trail Mix
$2\frac{3}{4}$ cups grain cereal
$\frac{1}{3}$ cup nuts
$1\frac{1}{2}$ cups raisins

Find the total amount of trail mix she will make. Show your work.

Solution:

_____

15. Marco had $5\frac{7}{12}$ gallons of paint. He used $3\frac{4}{12}$ gallons. How much paint does he have left?

Use pictures, words, or numbers to show your work.

Solution: Marco has _____ gallons of paint left.

Explain how you found your answer.

_____

_____

_____

_____

How can you add decimal numbers?

Explore

Decimal numbers use the base-ten system to show parts of a whole. The place-value chart shows the value of each digit in 1.25 and 5.458.

How can you add decimal numbers?

1.25 + 5.458

Ones	Tenths	Hundredths	Thousandths
1	2	5	0
5	4	5	8

Think

1.25 has __1__ one, __2__ tenths, __5__ hundredths, and __0__ thousandths.

5.458 has __5__ ones, __4__ tenths, __5__ hundredths, and __8__ thousandths.

Estimate the **sum** by rounding each number to the nearest whole number.

1.25 rounds to __1__, and 5.458 rounds to __5__.

The actual sum should be close to __5__ + __1__ = __6__.

Rewrite the problem vertically. Align the decimal points so that place values match up.

$$\begin{array}{r} 1.250 \\ + 5.458 \end{array}$$ ← Use 0 as a placeholder.

Connect

Adding decimal numbers is similar to adding whole numbers. Add corresponding place values. Regroup as needed.

Step 1: 0 thousandths + 8 thousandths = 8 thousandths

Step 2: 5 hundredths + 5 hundredths = 10 hundredths
Regroup as 1 tenth.

Step 3: 2 tenths + 4 tenths + 1 regrouped tenth = 7 tenths

Step 4: 1 one + 5 ones = 6 ones

The sum is 6.708, which is close to the estimate of 6.

$$\begin{array}{r} {}^{1} \\ 1.250 \\ + 5.458 \\ \hline 6.708 \end{array}$$

Let's Talk

How is adding decimal numbers similar to adding whole numbers? Give an example to explain your answer.

Fill in the blanks. Solve the problem.

What is the sum of 3.46 and 1.064?

■ Find 3.46 + 1.064.

■ 3.46 has _____ ones, _____ tenths, _____ hundredths,
 and _____ thousandths.

 1.064 has _____ one, _____ tenths, _____ hundredths,
 and _____ thousandths.

■ Estimate.   3.46 rounds to _____.
 1.064 rounds to _____.

 The sum should be close to _____ + _____ = _____.

■ Rewrite the problem vertically. Align the numbers by
 decimal point. Then add.

> Use the tenths digit to help you round.
> If the digit in the tenths place is 5 or greater, increase the ones digit. If the digit in the tenths place is 4 or less, keep the ones digit the same.

1. Add 0 thousandths and 4 thousandths.	
2. Add 6 hundredths and 6 hundredths.	☐.☐☐☐
3. Add 1 regrouped tenth and 4 tenths and 0 tenths.	+ ☐.☐☐☐
4. Add 3 ones and 1 one.	☐.☐☐☐

Solution: The sum is _____, which is close to the estimate of _____.

Your Turn ▷ **Now, use what you know to solve this problem.**

 1. Which number is the sum of 6.028 and 3.476?

 Ⓐ 9.252

 Ⓑ 9.404

 Ⓒ 9.494

 Ⓓ 9.504

 **How can you subtract decimal numbers?**

Explore

Whole numbers have no fraction or decimal parts. To subtract whole numbers, align the numbers so that place values match up.

$$2{,}056 - 487 \rightarrow \quad \begin{array}{r} \overset{1}{} \overset{9}{} \overset{14}{} \overset{16}{} \\ 2{,}056 \\ -\ 487 \\ \hline 1{,}569 \end{array}$$

How can you subtract decimal numbers?

$$4.193 - 1.52$$

Think

Estimate the **difference** by rounding each number to the nearest whole number.

4.193 rounds to __4__, and 1.52 rounds to __2__.

The actual difference should be close to __4__ − __2__ = __2__.

Rewrite the problem vertically. Align the numbers by decimal point so that place values match up.

$$\boxed{4} . \boxed{1}\,\boxed{9}\,\boxed{3}$$
$$-\boxed{1} . \boxed{5}\,\boxed{2}\,\boxed{0}$$

Connect

Subtract decimal numbers the same way you subtract whole numbers. Subtract by place value. Regroup as needed.

Step 1: 3 thousandths − 0 thousandths = 3 thousandths

Step 2: 9 hundredths − 2 hundredths = 7 hundredths

Step 3: Regroup 4 ones and 1 tenth as 3 ones and 11 tenths.

Step 4: 11 tenths − 5 tenths = 6 tenths

Step 5: 3 ones − 1 one = 2 ones

$$\begin{array}{r} \overset{3}{}\overset{11}{} \\ 4.193 \\ -1.520 \\ \hline 2.673 \end{array}$$

The difference is 2.673, which is close to the estimate of 2.

Let's Talk

Why was a zero written after 1.52 in the subtraction problem? Explain why 1.52 and 1.520 have the same value.

Fill in the blanks. Solve the problem.

How much greater is 5.783 than 2.392?

■ Find 5.783 − 2.392.

■ Estimate. 5.783 rounds to _____.

2.392 rounds to _____.

The difference should be close to _____ − _____ = _____.

■ Rewrite the problem vertically. Align the numbers by decimal point. Then subtract.

> **1.** Find 3 thousandths − 2 thousandths.
>
> **2.** Regroup 7 tenths 8 hundredths as 6 tenths 18 hundredths.
>
> **3.** Find 18 hundredths − 9 hundredths.
>
> **4.** Find 6 tenths − 3 tenths.
>
> **5.** Find 5 ones − 2 ones.

Solution: The difference is _____, which is close to the estimate of _____.

Your Turn Now, use what you know to solve this problem.

2. Subtract 2.4 from 5.118. What is the difference?

Show your work.

> Because 2.4 is being subtracted *from* 5.118, write 5.118 as the top number in the subtraction.

5.118 − 2.4 = _____

Solve the problem. Then read why each answer choice is correct or not correct.

Solve

A snail crawled 3.428 decimeters. Then it turned right and crawled another 2.109 decimeters.

How far did the snail crawl in all?

Ⓐ 1.319 dm

Ⓑ 5.527 dm

Ⓒ 5.537 dm

Ⓓ 5.618 dm

Connect

Check to see if you chose the correct answer.

Find 3.428 + 2.109.

Rewrite the problem vertically and align the place values.
Add each place value from right to left, regrouping as needed.

$$
\begin{array}{r}
3.4\overset{1}{2}8 \\
+\ 2.109 \\
\hline
5.537
\end{array}
$$

Regroup 17 thousandths as 1 hundredth and 7 thousandths.

So, the correct answer is Ⓒ.

Why are the other answer choices not correct?

Ⓐ 1.319 dm	This is the difference, not the sum.
Ⓑ 5.527 dm	Remember to include the regrouped hundredth: 1 + 2 + 0 = 3 hundredths, not 2.
Ⓓ 5.618 dm	The addend 2.19 was used instead of the addend 2.109.

Solve each problem. Use the hints to avoid mistakes.

- Determine if you need to add or subtract.
- Write the problem vertically so that the decimal points are aligned.
- Use zeros as placeholders so the decimals have the same number of digits.
- Regroup across place values as needed, just like you would with whole numbers.

3. Which is the sum of 3.426 and 3.581?

Ⓐ 6.007

Ⓑ 6.907

Ⓒ 7.007

Ⓓ 7.07

4. A scientist had 8.432 grams of salt. She used 6.02 grams of salt in an experiment. How much salt does the scientist have left over?

Ⓐ 2.012 g

Ⓑ 2.412 g

Ⓒ 7.830 g

Ⓓ 14.452 g

5. Which of these expressions has a sum of 9.748?

Ⓐ 5.23 + 4.518

Ⓑ 6.391 + 3.507

Ⓒ 2.869 + 5.249

Ⓓ 4.708 + 3.160

6. Mr. Gustavo wrote this equation on the board:

7.329 − ▢ = 4.844

Which number is missing from the equation?

Ⓐ 2.485

Ⓑ 2.585

Ⓒ 3.525

Ⓓ 12.173

Study the model. It is a good example of a written answer.

Student Model

Show

Amy needs to drive 9 kilometers to the store. She stopped after 6.94 kilometers to get gas. How much farther does she need to drive to get to the store?

Use pictures, words, or numbers to show your work.

Estimate. 6.94 rounds to 7. $9 - 7 = 2$

Write 9 to the hundredths place. 9.00

Rewrite the problem. Align the numbers.

$$
\begin{array}{r}
\overset{8}{\cancel{9}}.\overset{9}{\cancel{0}}\overset{10}{\cancel{0}} \\
-\ 6.94 \\
\hline
2.06
\end{array}
$$

The difference is 2.06, close to 2.

Solution: Amy still needs to drive __2.06__ kilometers.

Explain

Explain how you got your answer.

I had to find the difference of 9 and 6.94. First, I rounded

the decimal number to estimate the difference. Then, I wrote

9 as 9.00. Next, I wrote the subtraction problem vertically

by aligning the decimal points and place values. I regrouped

9.00 as 8 ones, 9 tenths, and 10 hundredths. I subtracted

one place value at a time, from right to left. My answer was

close to the estimate, so I knew it was reasonable.

☑ The student shows each step.

☑ The student correctly answers the question asked.

☑ The student gives important details about how to find the difference.

☑ The student uses the math words *difference*, *decimal number*, and *estimate*.

7. A swimmer finished a race in 9.71 seconds. This was 0.12 seconds longer than the first-place swimmer. How long did it take the first-place swimmer to finish the race?

Use pictures, words, or numbers to show your work.

> ☑ CHECKLIST
>
> Did you . . .
>
> ☐ show each step?
>
> ☐ answer the question asked?
>
> ☐ give important details?
>
> ☐ use math words?

Solution: The first-place swimmer finished in _____ seconds.

Explain how you got your answer.

_____

_____

_____

_____

_____

As you solve decimal problems, remember to
- read the problem twice to determine if you need to find a sum or a difference. Either way, you should align the digits by place value.
- use zeros as placeholders when necessary.
- check that you placed the decimal point in the answer.

Solve each problem.

8. Paulo is making a model of a building. He places the model on a stand as shown.

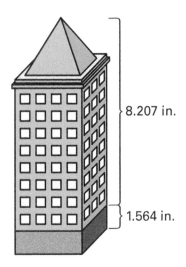

8.207 in.

1.564 in.

What is the total height of the model, including the stand?

Ⓐ 9.761 in.   Ⓒ 9.771 in.

Ⓑ 9.763 in.   Ⓓ 9.834 in.

9. When 5.108 is added to a number, the sum is 6.472. What is the number?

Ⓐ 0.374   Ⓒ 1.364

Ⓑ 0.580   Ⓓ 1.376

10. Kevin bought a notebook for $2.59 and a box of pencils for $1.27. How much did he spend in all?

Ⓐ $1.32

Ⓑ $3.72

Ⓒ $3.76

Ⓓ $3.86

11. A jeweler had 5.375 ounces of gold. She used 2.4 ounces to make a bracelet. How much gold does the jeweler have left?

Ⓐ 2.975 oz

Ⓑ 3.175 oz

Ⓒ 3.371 oz

Ⓓ 5.351 oz

12. Christina scored 8.746 on her gymnastics routine. Amanda scored 7.459. How much higher was Christina's score?

Ⓐ 1.195

Ⓑ 1.287

Ⓒ 1.297

Ⓓ 1.313

13. What is the sum of 4.541 and 6.8?

Ⓐ 11.429

Ⓑ 11.341

Ⓒ 10.549

Ⓓ 10.341

14. Hector hiked 4.18 miles on Monday. He hiked 3.49 miles on Tuesday.

Estimate how far he hiked in all, and then find the exact sum.
Show your work.

Estimate:

_____ miles

Exact Sum:

_____ miles

15. Amir's scores in a diving competition were 8.0, 7.6, and 8.325. What is his total score?

Use pictures, words, or numbers to show your work.

Solution: Amir's total score is _____.

Explain how you found your answer.

_____

_____

_____

_____

PART **ONE:** Learn About Area of a Parallelogram

 How can you use a rectangle to find the area of a parallelogram?

Explore

Area (*A*) tells how much surface a two-dimensional figure covers. You can use the **formula** $A = l \times w$ to find the area of a rectangle. How can you find the area of a parallelogram?

Think

A **parallelogram** has four sides. The opposite sides are **parallel**. They are the same distance apart and never meet.

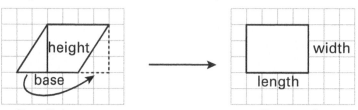

Parallelogram   Rectangle

If you cut a triangle off of one end and move it to the other end, you get _a rectangle_.

In the parallelogram, $b =$ __4__ units and $h =$ __3__ units.

In the rectangle, $l =$ __4__ units and $w =$ __3__ units.

Connect

The parallelogram and rectangle cover the same area on the grid.

Instead of $A = l \times w$, you can use $A = b \times h$ to find the area of a parallelogram.

$A = b \times h$

$A = 4 \times 3$

$A = 12$ square units

Figure	Dimensions	Formula
Parallelogram	*b* and *h*	$A = b \times h$
Rectangle	*l* and *w*	$A = l \times w$

Let's Talk

If you know the area of a parallelogram and its base, how can you find its height? Explain.

Fill in the blanks. Solve the problem.

Gino is going to pave his patio. It is in the shape
of a parallelogram.

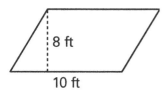

What is the area Gino needs to pave?

■ Find the dimensions.

In the parallelogram, $b =$ _____ feet and $h =$ _____ feet.

■ Use the formula for the area of a parallelogram.

$A =$ _____ × _____

$A =$ _____ × _____

$A =$ _____ square feet

Solution: Gino needs to pave _____ square feet of his patio.

> The base and height of a parallelogram always form a **right angle.** Sometimes the height of the parallelogram is not one of the sides.

Your Turn Now, use what you know to solve this problem.

1. What is the area of this parallelogram?

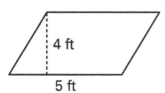

Ⓐ 1 sq ft

Ⓑ 9 sq ft

Ⓒ 13 sq ft

Ⓓ 20 sq ft

 **How can you find the area of a triangle?**

Explore

You can use the formula $A = b \times h$ to find the area of a parallelogram. How can you use the area of a parallelogram to find the area of a triangle?

Think

A **triangle** is a polygon with three sides. If you draw a second triangle with the same size and shape, you can form a ___parallelogram___. The triangles are **congruent**.

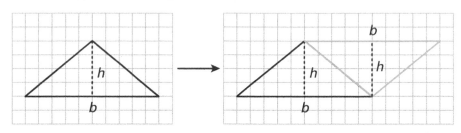

The base of each triangle is __10__ units. The height of each triangle is __4__ units. What fraction of the parallelogram is taken up by each triangle? __$\frac{1}{2}$__

Connect

The parallelogram and the two triangles cover the same area on the grid. The area of the parallelogram is $A = b \times h$, so the area of one triangle must be $A = \frac{1}{2}(b \times h)$.

The base and height of each triangle are the base and height of the parallelogram.

$A = \frac{1}{2}(b \times h)$

$A = \frac{1}{2}(10 \times 4)$

$A = \frac{1}{2}(40) = 20$ square units

Let's Talk

How can you check the example to prove that the area of each triangle is $\frac{1}{2}$ the area of the parallelogram? Use your method to show that the answer is correct.

Fill in the blanks. Solve the problem.

Alexis is making a garden in the shape of a triangle.

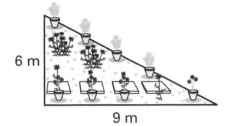

6 m

9 m

What is the area of her garden?

■ Alexis can draw a second triangle that is _____ to her garden. She can arrange the triangles into a _____.

■ The height of the parallelogram is _____ meters.
The base of the parallelogram is _____ meters.

■ The area of the triangle is _____ the area of the parallelogram.
The area of the parallelogram is $A = b \times h$,

so the area of the triangle is $A =$ _____ $(b \times h)$.

Use the formula to find the area.

$A =$ _____ (_____ $\times$ _____)

$A =$ _____

Solution: The area of Alexis's garden is _____ square meters.

> Just like the parallelogram, the base and height of the triangle must form a right angle. In this case, the height of the triangle is a side of the triangle.

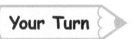 Now, use what you know to solve this problem.

2. What is the area of this triangle? Use the formula.

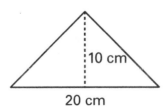

10 cm

20 cm

$A =$ _____ (_____ $\times$ _____)

$A =$ _____ $= 100$ sq cm

Solve the problem. Then read why each answer choice is correct or not correct.

Solve

Mr. Sanchez is painting shapes on his son's wall. One shape is this triangle.

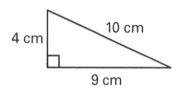

Which equation shows how to find the area of the triangle?

Ⓐ $4 + 9 = 13$

Ⓑ $9 \times 4 = 36$

Ⓒ $9 + 4 + 10 = 23$

Ⓓ $\frac{1}{2} \times 9 \times 4 = 18$

Check

Check to see if you chose the correct answer.

The base of the triangle is 9 centimeters, and the height is 4 centimeters.

$A = \frac{1}{2}(b \times h)$

$A = \frac{1}{2}(9 \times 4) = 18$

So, the correct answer is Ⓓ.

Why are the other answer choices not correct?

Ⓐ $4 + 9 = 13$	This is the sum of the base and height. To find the area, multiply $\frac{1}{2}$ by the product of the base and height.
Ⓑ $9 \times 4 = 36$	The product of base and height must be multiplied by $\frac{1}{2}$.
Ⓒ $9 + 4 + 10 = 23$	This is the perimeter of the triangle. Use the formula for area.

Solve each problem. Use the hints to avoid mistakes.

- Choose the correct formula to find the area of a parallelogram or a triangle.
- Identify the measurements for the base and height of the figure.
- Replace the variables in the formula with the measurements and solve.

3. Olivia drew this parallelogram.

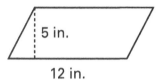

5 in.

12 in.

Which expression can you use to find the area of the parallelogram?

Ⓐ 12 + 5 + 12 + 5

Ⓑ $\frac{1}{2}(12 \times 5)$

Ⓒ 12 + 5

Ⓓ 12 × 5

4. A store sells a carpet in the shape of a parallelogram.

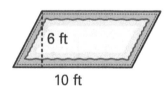

6 ft

10 ft

What is the area of the carpet?

Ⓐ   16 sq ft

Ⓑ   30 sq ft

Ⓒ   60 sq ft

Ⓓ   106 sq ft

5. A restaurant has a table in the shape of a triangle.

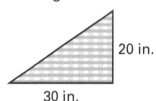

20 in.

30 in.

Which expression can you use to find the area of the table?

Ⓐ $\frac{1}{2}(30 \times 20)$

Ⓑ 30 × 20

Ⓒ $\frac{1}{2}(30 + 20)$

Ⓓ 30 + 20

6. A triangle has a height of 14 inches and a base of 8 inches. What is the area of the triangle?

Ⓐ   11 sq in.

Ⓑ   22 sq in.

Ⓒ   56 sq in.

Ⓓ   112 sq in.

Study the model. It is a good example of a written answer.

Student Model

Show

Riley is planting grass seed in the yard shown in the picture. What is the area of the yard that Riley is planting?

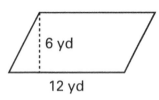

6 yd

12 yd

Use pictures, words, or numbers to show your work.

$A = b \times h$

$\qquad b = 12$ and $h = 6$

$A = 12 \times 6$

$A = 72$

> ☑ The student shows each step.

Solution: ___72___ square yards

> ☑ The student correctly answers the question asked.

Explain

Explain how you got your answer.

Because the shape of Riley's yard is a parallelogram,

I used the formula $A = b \times h$. The base is 12 yards and

the height is 6 yards. I put those values into the formula

and then found the area: $12 \times 6 = 72$. So, the area is

72 square yards.

> ☑ The student gives important details about how to find the area.

> ☑ The student uses the math words *parallelogram, formula, base, height,* and *area.*

7. Pedro drew this shape on a poster. What is the area of the shape?

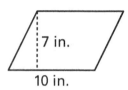

7 in.

10 in.

Use pictures, words, or numbers to show your work.

☑ CHECKLIST

Did you . . .

☐ show each step?

☐ answer the question asked?

☐ give important details?

☐ use math words?

Solution: _____ square inches

Explain how you got your answer.

_____

_____

_____

_____

_____

As you solve area problems, remember to
- draw a picture of the figure if one is not given.
- write the formula you will use. Then solve the problem.
- check your work by using division.

Solve each problem.

8. Which expression can be used to find the area of the parallelogram?

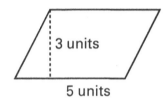

3 units

5 units

Ⓐ 5 + 3

Ⓑ 5 + 3 + 5 + 3

Ⓒ 5 − 3

Ⓓ 5 × 3

9. Which equation can be used to find the area of the triangle?

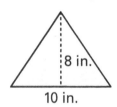

8 in.

10 in.

Ⓐ 10 − 2 = 8

Ⓑ 10 + 8 = 18

Ⓒ $\frac{1}{2}(10 \times 8) = 40$

Ⓓ 10 × 8 = 80

10. Which parallelogram has an area of 18 square units?

Ⓐ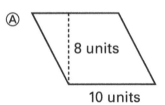

8 units

10 units

Ⓑ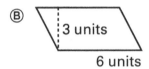

3 units

6 units

Ⓒ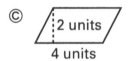

2 units

4 units

Ⓓ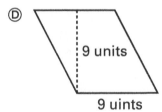

9 units

9 uints

11. A parallelogram has a base of 8 centimeters. Its area is 24 square centimeters. What is the height of the parallelogram?

Ⓐ 3 cm

Ⓑ 6 cm

Ⓒ 8 cm

Ⓓ 12 cm

Geometry and Measurement

12. Mrs. Ramirez drew this shape with chalk on the playground.

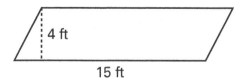

4 ft

15 ft

What is the area of the shape?

Ⓐ 60 sq ft   Ⓒ 19 sq ft

Ⓑ 30 sq ft   Ⓓ 11 sq ft

13. A marching band is forming a triangle with a base of 10 yards and a height of 3 yards. What is the area of the triangle?

Ⓐ 13 sq yd   Ⓒ 23 sq yd

Ⓑ 15 sq yd   Ⓓ 30 sq yd

14. Tyrone's family is going camping. The picture shows their tent.

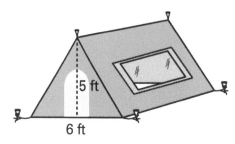

5 ft

6 ft

Write an equation to find the area of the front of the tent.

_____

$A =$ _____ square feet

15. Joshua's front yard forms a triangle. The base of the triangle is 12 yards. The height of the triangle is 8 yards. What is the area of Joshua's front yard?

Use pictures, words, or numbers to show your work.

Solution: _____ square yards

Explain how you found your answer.

_____

_____

_____

_____

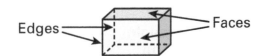 **What does a net show you about rectangular prisms?**

Explore

A **rectangular prism** is a solid figure with rectangles for all of its surfaces.

The surfaces, called **faces**, meet in line segments, called **edges**.

Edges — — Faces

Opposite faces are **congruent**. They have the same shape and size.

What would a rectangular prism look like if it were flattened?

Think

A rectangular prism has 3 dimensions.

How many dimensions does a flat figure have? __2__

Suppose you make a flat pattern of a rectangular prism.

■ How many faces will it show? __6__

■ What shape is every face? __a rectangle__

Connect

If you cut along some of the edges of a prism and make a flat pattern, you get a net.

A **net** shows you a 2-dimensional view of a 3-dimensional figure.

net of a rectangular prism

Let's Talk

This is the same net, with the faces labeled.

What pairs of faces are congruent?

Do the congruent faces in this prism meet?

Why do these two edges have the same length?

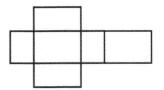

Fill in the blanks. Solve the problem.

Kim made a net from this cardboard box. She cut along some of the edges and flattened the box. She started to draw a picture of the net, as shown on the right.

 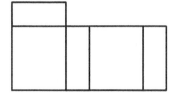

incomplete net

Finish Kim's drawing of the net.

The edges of the net that meet to form the prism are the same length.

■ How many dimensions will the net have? _____

■ How many faces will the net have? _____

■ What shape is every face? _____

■ Opposite faces of a rectangular prism do not meet. What is true about opposite faces of a rectangular prism? They are _____.

Solution: Finish the drawing of the net.

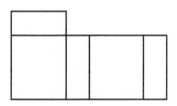

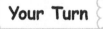 **Now, use what you know to solve this problem.**

1. Which is a net of this prism?

Ⓐ

Ⓒ

Ⓑ

Ⓓ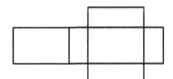

How can you use what you know about area and nets to find the surface area of a rectangular prism?

Explore

A rectangular prism has 6 faces that are all rectangles.

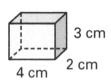

3 cm

2 cm

4 cm

The area of a rectangle is length × width.

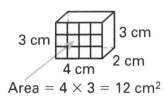

3 cm   3 cm

4 cm   2 cm

Area = 4 × 3 = 12 cm²

The **surface area** of a prism is the total area of all its faces.

How can you find the total area of all the faces of a prism?

Think

How can you show all the faces of a prism? Draw a ___net___ of the prism.

How can you find the area of each face? Find ___length × width___.

How can you find the surface area of a prism?
Add the ___areas___ of all the ___faces___.

Connect

To find the surface area of a prism, find the areas of all 6 faces and then add.

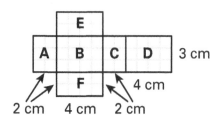

E

A   B   C   D   3 cm

F   4 cm

2 cm   4 cm   2 cm

Face		Area
A	2 × 3 =	6 cm²
B	4 × 3 =	12 cm²
C	2 × 3 =	6 cm²
D	4 × 3 =	12 cm²
E	4 × 2 =	8 cm²
F	4 × 2 =	+8 cm²
Surface Area of Prism =		52 cm²

Let's Talk

What faces of the rectangular prism above are congruent?
How can you use congruent faces to find the surface area by a shorter method?

Fill in the blanks. Solve the problem.

Leon keeps his sports equipment in this wood box.
He wants to paint all faces of the box to protect the wood.
What is the surface area Leon needs to paint?

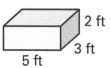
2 ft
3 ft
5 ft

■ You have to find the surface area of a rectangular prism.

The surface area of a prism is the sum of the areas of all its _____.

■ To show all the faces, you can draw a _____ of the prism.

To find the area of each face, you can find _____.

To find the surface area, you can _____ the areas of all the faces.

■ Complete the net and label the dimensions. Then find the surface area.

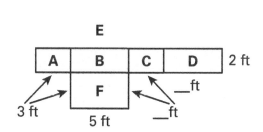

E

| A | B | C | D | 2 ft
| | F | | |
3 ft   5 ft   __ft   __ft

Face				Area
A	3	×	2	=	6 ft²
B	5	×	2	=	___ ft²
C	3	×	2	=	___ ft²
D	___	×	___	=	___ ft²
E	___	×	___	=	___ ft²
F	___	×	___	=	+ ___ ft²
Surface Area of Prism				=	___ ft²

> You can add the areas of faces A, B, and E. Then double that sum to find the surface area.

Solution: Leon needs to paint _____ of surface area.

Your Turn ⟩ **Now, use what you know to solve this problem.**

2. Find the surface area of this rectangular prism.
Draw a net of the prism to help you find the areas
you need to add.

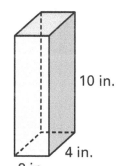
10 in.
4 in.
3 in.

Surface area = _____ in.²

Solve the problem. Then read why each answer choice is correct or not correct.

Explore

A worker made this cardboard box for her cereal company.

What is the amount of cardboard in the surface area of the box?

Ⓐ   900 cm²

Ⓑ 1,200 cm²

Ⓒ 1,800 cm²

Ⓓ 3,600 cm²

Connect

Check to see if you chose the correct answer.

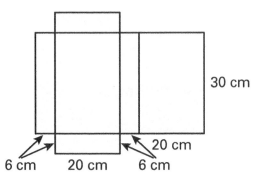

$6 \times 30 =$	180 cm²
$20 \times 30 =$	600 cm²
$6 \times 30 =$	180 cm²
$20 \times 30 =$	600 cm²
$20 \times 6 =$	120 cm²
$20 \times 6 =$	+120 cm²

Surface Area of Prism = 1,800 cm²

So, the correct answer is Ⓒ.

Why are the other answer choices not correct?

Ⓐ 900 cm²	This is the sum of the areas of only 3 faces. $180 + 600 + 120 = 900$
Ⓑ 1,200 cm²	This is the sum of the areas of only 5 faces. $180 + 600 + 120 + 180 + 120 = 1,200$
Ⓓ 3,600 cm²	This is the product of the dimensions. $20 \times 6 \times 30 = 3,600$

- When identifying a net for a rectangular prism, check that opposite faces are congruent and matching edges have the same length.
- Multiply 2 dimensions to find the area of each face. Then add to find the surface area.
- Read the problem carefully to decide if you need to find the total surface area.

3. Terrell wants to make a box with a square top and bottom.

← square

Which net can he fold to make the box?

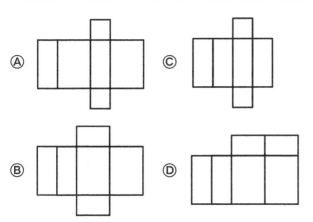

Ⓐ   Ⓒ   Ⓑ   Ⓓ

4. What is the surface area of this rectangular prism?

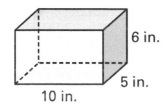

6 in.
5 in.
10 in.

Ⓐ 140 in.²   Ⓒ 280 in.²

Ⓑ 220 in.²   Ⓓ 300 in.²

5. Emma has this net for a box.

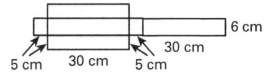

6 cm
30 cm
5 cm   30 cm   5 cm

Which box can she make from the net?

Ⓐ 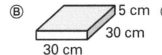 6 cm
30 cm   5 cm

Ⓒ 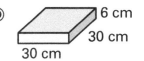 5 cm
30 cm   5 cm

Ⓑ 5 cm
30 cm
30 cm

Ⓓ 6 cm
30 cm
30 cm

6. Alex has a cabinet in the shape of a cube. He wants to paint every face except the bottom. What is the surface area he will paint?

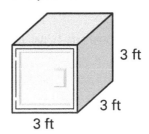

3 ft
3 ft
3 ft

Ⓐ 27 ft²   Ⓒ 45 ft²

Ⓑ 30 ft²   Ⓓ 54 ft²

Study the model. It is a good example of a written answer.

Student Model

Show

Miko wants to cover this brick with special cloth to make a doorstop.

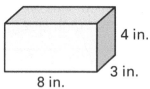

What amount of cloth does Miko need to cover the brick?

Show your work. Include a drawing of a net.

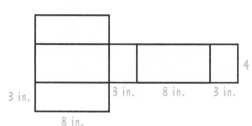

Areas of three faces:

$8 \times 3 = 24$ in.²
$3 \times 4 = 12$ in.²
$8 \times 4 = +\,32$ in.²
$ 68$ in.²

68 in.²
$\underline{\times 2}$
Surface area $= 136$ in.²

> ☑ The student shows a diagram and each step.

> ☑ The student correctly answers the question asked.

Solution: Miko needs ___136 square inches___ of cloth.

Explain

Explain how you got your answer.

The amount of cloth Miko needs is the surface area of the

brick. I drew a net of the brick to help me see all the

faces. I multiplied length times width to find the area of

each different size face. I added the three areas and then

multiplied by 2 to find the surface area.

> ☑ The student gives important details about how to find the surface area.

> ☑ The student uses the math words *surface area, net,* and *face.*

7. Eric wrapped this package to mail it. What amount of wrapping paper covers the package?

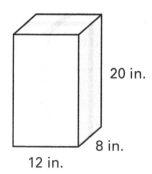

20 in.

8 in.

12 in.

Show your work. Include a drawing of a net.

CHECKLIST

Did you . . .

☐ show a diagram and each step?

☐ answer the question asked?

☐ give important details?

☐ use math words?

Solution: It takes _____ of wrapping paper to cover the package.

Explain how you got your answer.

_____

_____

_____

_____

_____

As you solve problems about rectangular prisms, remember that
- every rectangular prism has 6 faces that are all rectangles.
- opposite faces of a rectangular prism are congruent.
- in a net, matching edges must be the same length.
- the surface area of a prism is the sum of the areas of all faces.

Solve each problem.

8. Which net can be used to make this box?

Ⓐ   Ⓒ

Ⓑ   Ⓓ

9. The net for the prism is incomplete.

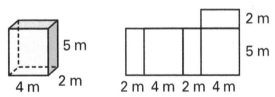

Which figure completes the net?

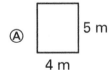

Ⓐ   5 m   Ⓒ   5 m
    4 m   2 m

Ⓑ   2 m   Ⓓ   5 m
    4 m   5 m

10. How much cardboard makes up the surface area of this box?

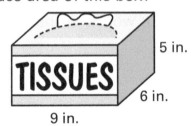

5 in.

6 in.

9 in.

Ⓐ   80 in.^{2} Ⓒ   258 in.^{2}

Ⓑ   129 in.^{2} Ⓓ   270 in.^{2}

11. Julio has this pattern for a box.

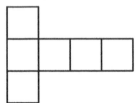

Which box can Julio make?

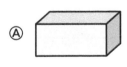

Ⓐ   Ⓒ

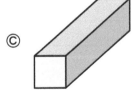

Ⓑ   Ⓓ

12. This wood crate holds salt for icy roads.

4 ft
4 ft
4 ft

How much wood is needed to make the crate?

Ⓐ 48 ft²   Ⓒ 80 ft²

Ⓑ 64 ft²   Ⓓ 96 ft²

13. What is the surface area of this plastic storage bin?

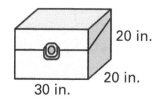

20 in.
20 in.
30 in.

Ⓐ 2,600 in.²   Ⓒ 3,200 in.²

Ⓑ 2,800 in.²   Ⓓ 3,800 in.²

14. Rick is planning to build a dog house without a floor. He will choose one of the plans below.

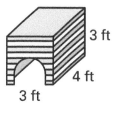
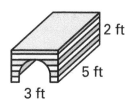

3 ft
4 ft
3 ft

2 ft
5 ft
3 ft

Plan A   **Plan B**

Rick will build the dog house, and then cut the hole in the front. Which plan will use less wood? Show your work.

_____

15. Aisha has a rectangular sheet of wrapping paper 40 inches long and 30 inches wide. Does she have enough paper to cover this box?

Show your work. Include a drawing of a net.

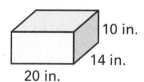

10 in.
14 in.
20 in.

Solution: Aisha _____ have enough wrapping paper to cover the box.

Explain how you found your answer.

_____

_____

_____

_____

 **How can you find the volume of a rectangular prism?**

Explore

You can find the **area** of a rectangle by counting the number of square units that cover the surface completely.

 =1 square unit   8 square units

How can you find the amount of space inside a **rectangular prism**?

Think

rectangular prism

   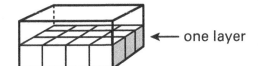 ← one layer

=1 cubic unit

Count the number of **cubic units** in each layer of the rectangular prism.

How many cubic units are in the bottom layer? __12__

How many cubic units are in the top layer? __12__

You have __2__ layers. Each layer has __12__ cubic units.

Connect

You can find the **volume** of a rectangular prism by counting the number of cubic units in each layer. Then add to find the total number of cubic units.

12 cubic units in the bottom + 12 cubic units in the top = 24 cubic units in all

Let's Talk

How is a cubic inch like a cubic centimeter? How is it different?

Fill in the blanks. Solve the problem.

Travis has a rectangular prism filled with cubic units.

rectangular prism

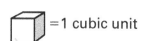=1 cubic unit 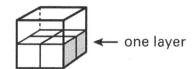 ← one layer

What is the volume of the rectangular prism?

■ Count the number of cubic units in each layer.

How many cubic units are in the bottom layer? _____

How many cubic units are in the top layer? _____

■ Add the number of cubic units in each layer to find the total.

There are _____ cubic units in each layer.

Add: _____ cubic units + _____ cubic units = _____ cubic units

Solution: The volume of the rectangular prism is _____ cubic units.

> You can't always see all the cubes in a drawing of a rectangular prism, so try to imagine what one layer looks like. All the layers in a prism have the same number of cubes.

Your Turn Now, use what you know to solve this problem.

1. What is the volume of the rectangular prism?

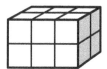

  Ⓐ   2 cubic units

  Ⓑ   3 cubic units

  Ⓒ   6 cubic units

  Ⓓ 12 cubic units

What formula can you use to find the volume
of a rectangular prism?

Explore

The area of a rectangle can be found by multiplying the length by
the width.

4 cm

1 cm

Area: 4 cm × 1 cm = 4 cm²

How does the area of a rectangle relate to the volume of a rectangular prism?

Think

2 cm

1 cm

4 cm

What shape is the base of a rectangular
prism? __rectangle__

Multiply __length__ by __width__ to find the
area of the base.

Imagine filling the prism with blocks.

How many layers of blocks will there be? __2__

What is the height of the prism? __2 cm__

Connect

To find the volume of a rectangular prism, multiply the area of the base
of the prism by its height.

Use the **formula** $V = Bh$. This is the same as $V = l \times w \times h$.

The dimensions are: $l = 4$ cm,
$w = 1$ cm, $h = 2$ cm.

$V = l \times w \times h$

$V = 4 \times 1 \times 2$

$V = 8$

The volume of the rectangular prism is 8 cm³.

2 cm

1 cm

4 cm

Let's Talk

Explain why Bh is the same as $l \times w \times h$.

Is B measured in square units or cubic units?

Fill in the blanks. Solve the problem.

A rectangular baking dish measures 9 inches by 13 inches by 2 inches.

Use the volume formula to find the volume of the dish.

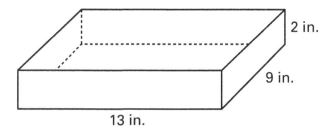

2 in.

9 in.

13 in.

■ Find the dimensions.

length (l) = _____

width (w) = _____

height (h) = _____

■ Write the volume formula $V = Bh$ or

$V =$ _____ × _____ × _____.

■ Put the values for l, w, and h into the formula.

$V =$ _____ × _____ × _____

■ Solve.

$V =$ _____

Solution: The volume of the baking dish is _____ cubic inches.

"cm³" is read *centimeters cubed.* That means that the unit of measure is three-dimensional, like a cube— not two-dimensional, like a square.

Now, use what you know to solve this problem.

2. Use the formula to find the volume of the prism.

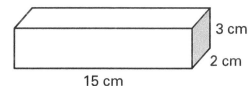

3 cm

2 cm

15 cm

The volume of the rectangular prism is _____ cm³.

Solve the problem. Then read why each answer choice is correct or not correct.

Solve

A shoe box has a length of 11 inches, a width of 6 inches, and a height of 4 inches.

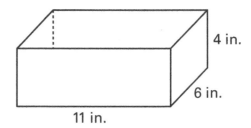

4 in.

6 in.

11 in.

Which number sentence shows the volume of the shoe box?

Ⓐ $11 + 6 + 4 = 21$ in.³

Ⓑ $11 \times 6 \times 4 = 244$ in.³

Ⓒ $11 \times 6 \times 4 = 264$ in.³

Ⓓ $66 + 66 + 44 + 44 + 24 + 24 = 268$ in.³

Check

Check to see if you chose the correct answer.

Find volume using the formula $V = Bh$, which is the same as $V = l \times w \times h$.

Put the values for l, w, and h into the formula and solve.

$V = l \times w \times h$

$l = 11, w = 6, h = 4$

$V = 11 \times 6 \times 4$

$V = 264$ in.³

So, the correct answer is Ⓒ.

Why are the other answer choices not correct?

Ⓐ $11 + 6 + 4 = 21$ in.³	The dimensions should be multiplied, not added.
Ⓑ $11 \times 6 \times 4 = 244$ in.³	$66 \times 4 = 264$, not 244.
Ⓓ $66 + 66 + 44 + 44 + 24 + 24 = 268$ in.³	This is the surface area, not the volume.

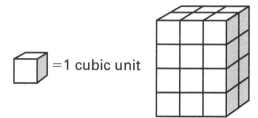

• To find the number of cubic units in a figure, count the number of cubes in each layer, and then add.

• Identify the length, width, and height of each prism. Use the volume formula to solve.

3. What is the volume of the rectangular prism?

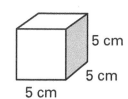 =1 cubic unit

Ⓐ 24 cubic units

Ⓑ 12 cubic units

Ⓒ   8 cubic units

Ⓓ   6 cubic units

4. Benjamin has a cube with the dimensions shown. Which expression can be used to find the volume?

5 cm
5 cm
5 cm

Ⓐ 5 + 5

Ⓑ 5 + 5 + 5

Ⓒ 5 × 5

Ⓓ 5 × 5 × 5

5. A container is in the shape of a rectangular prism. The length is 5 inches, the width is 3 inches, and the height is 4 inches.

Which equation shows how to find the volume of the container?

Ⓐ $5 + 3 + 4 = 12$ in.³

Ⓑ $5 + 3 \times 4 = 17$ in.³

Ⓒ $5 \times 3 + 4 = 19$ in.³

Ⓓ $5 \times 3 \times 4 = 60$ in.³

6. Which equation shows one way to find the volume of this rectangular prism?

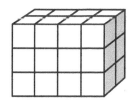

Ⓐ $2 + 2 + 2 = 6$

Ⓑ $4 + 4 + 4 = 12$

Ⓒ $8 + 8 + 8 = 24$

Ⓓ $8 \times 8 \times 8 = 512$

Study the model. It is a good example of a written answer.

Student Model

Show

Jayden's little brother built this figure out of cubes. What is the volume of the figure?

Use pictures, words, or numbers to show your work.

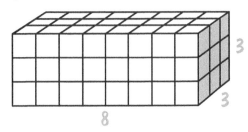

$3 \times 8 = 24$ cubes in one layer

3 layers in the prism

$24 + 24 + 24 = 72$ cubic units in all

Solution: ___72___ cubic units

☑ The student shows each step.

☑ The student correctly answers the question asked.

Explain

Explain how you got your answer.

The volume is the number of cubes that it takes to fill a

rectangular prism. I found the number of cubes that were

in each layer, and then added the cubes in each layer to

find the total. One layer has 3×8 cubes, or 24 cubes.

Then I added $24 + 24 + 24$ in the 3 layers to get

72 cubes in all.

☑ The student gives important details about how to find the volume.

☑ The student uses the math words *volume*, *cubes*, *rectangular prism*, and *add*.

7. This rectangular prism is made of cubes. What is the volume of the prism?

Use pictures, words, or numbers to show your work.

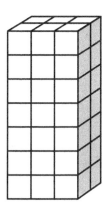

CHECKLIST

Did you . . .

- ☐ show each step?
- ☐ answer the question asked?
- ☐ give important details?
- ☐ use math words?

Solution: _____ cubic units

Explain how you got your answer.

_____

_____

_____

_____

_____

As you solve the volume problems, you may want to
- count the cubes in one layer, and then add the cubes in each layer to find the volume.
- use $V = Bh$, or $V = l \times w \times h$, to find the volume.

Solve each problem.

8. Stewart built a rectangular prism out of cubes. Which equation shows the volume of the prism?

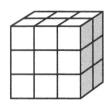

Ⓐ $6 + 6 + 6 = 18$

Ⓑ $3 + 3 + 3 = 9$

Ⓒ $2 + 2 + 2 = 6$

Ⓓ $3 \times 2 = 6$

9. What is volume of the prism?

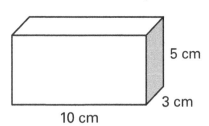

5 cm

3 cm

10 cm

Ⓐ 15 cm^3

Ⓑ 30 cm^3

Ⓒ 50 cm^3

Ⓓ 150 cm^3

10. Opal used cubes to fill a box that has the same length, width, and height. What is the volume of the box?

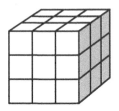

Ⓐ   6 cubic units

Ⓑ   9 cubic units

Ⓒ   27 cubic units

Ⓓ   54 cubic units

11. Amanda created a rectangular prism out of cubes with a length of 5, width of 2, and height of 3. Which expression shows how to find the volume?

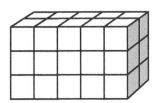

Ⓐ $5 + 2$

Ⓑ $5 + 2 + 3$

Ⓒ 5×2

Ⓓ $5 \times 2 \times 3$

12. Which of the following shows how to find the volume of the prism?

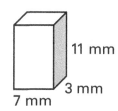

11 mm
3 mm
7 mm

Ⓐ $7 + 3 + 11 = 21$ mm³

Ⓑ $7 \times 3 \times 11 = 231$ mm³

Ⓒ $7 \times 3 = 21$ mm³

Ⓓ $7 \times 11 = 77$ mm³

13. The length of a box is 12 inches, the width is 11 inches, and the height is 2 inches. What is the volume of the box?

Ⓐ 264 in.³

Ⓑ 154 in.³

Ⓒ 35 in.³

Ⓓ 25 in.³

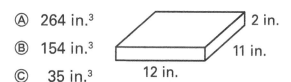

2 in.
11 in.
12 in.

14. Juliana's trunk is shaped like a rectangular prism. It is 4 feet long, 1 foot wide, and 2 feet high.

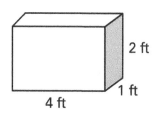

2 ft
1 ft
4 ft

Use the formula for the volume of a rectangular prism to write an expression for the volume of Juliana's trunk.

_____

What is the volume?

_____

15. Ling's pencil box is 25 centimeters by 2 centimeters by 3 centimeters. Label the box below with the correct dimensions. Then find the volume.

Use pictures, words, or numbers to show your work.

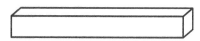

Solution: _____ cm³

Explain how you found your answer.

_____

_____

_____

_____

Lesson 16 LINE GRAPHS

PART ONE: Learn About Interpreting Line Graphs

 How can you read and interpret a line graph?

Explore

A **line plot** uses Xs above a number line to show how data are grouped. This line plot shows the number of pencils in 9 students' pencil cases. Each X represents one pencil case. Most data are grouped at 2 and 3 pencils.

How can you interpret data in a line *graph*?

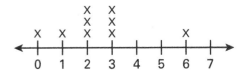

Think

A **line graph** shows **points** of data plotted on a graph and uses lines to connect the points.

On this line graph, each point represents a specific day and a temperature for that day. Look at the first three points (1, 70), (2, 64), and (3, 52).

On Day 1, the high temperature was __70__ °F. On Day 2, the high temperature was __64__ °F. On Day 3, the high temperature was __52__ °F.

Do the lines connecting these three points slant up or down as they go from left to right? __down__

Do the lines connecting (3, 52), (4, 60), and (5, 62) slant up or down as they go from left to right? __up__

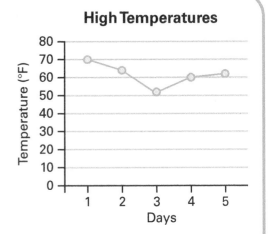

Connect

The lines connecting the points show how the data change over time. The lines slant down, so the temperature decreases from Day 1 to Day 3. The lines slant up, so the temperature increases from Day 3 to Day 5. The increase from Day 3 to Day 4 is greater than the increase from Day 4 to Day 5.

Let's Talk

How is a line graph different from a line plot?

Data Analysis

Fill in the blanks. Solve the problem.

Each year, researchers count the number of manatees living in a certain area. The data for five years are shown in the line graph. Between which two years did the number of manatees decrease?

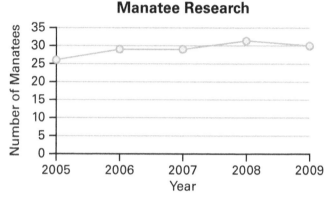

Manatee Research

The horizontal, or *x*-axis, in a line graph usually represents time.

■ Look at the points of data. How many manatees were counted in 2005? _____

In 2006? _____   In 2007? _____   In 2008? _____   In 2009? _____

■ Look at the lines between the data points. What do they show?

Between 2005 and 2006, the number of manatees increased by _____.

Between 2006 and 2007, the number of manatees _____.

Between 2007 and 2008, the number of manatees increased by _____.

Between 2008 and 2009, the number of manatees _____ by 1.

Solution: The number of manatees decreased between _____ and _____.

Your Turn **Now, use what you know to solve this problem.**

1. The graph represents the motion of an object. Where does the graph show an increase?

   Ⓐ   0 to 1 seconds

   Ⓑ   1 to 2 seconds

   Ⓒ   0 to 2 seconds

   Ⓓ   2 to 3 seconds

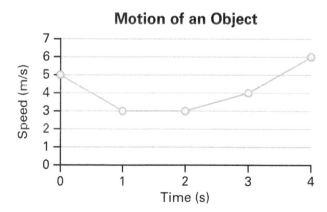

Motion of an Object

 **How can you create a line graph to display data?**

Explore

Tables can be used to organize data. The data in the table show the number of pages that Jacob read each day for 5 days. For example, he read 0 pages on Day 2.

How can you create a line graph to display these data?

Day	Pages
1	22
2	0
3	15
4	30
5	30

Think

Days will be shown on the _x-axis_. Number of pages will be shown on the _y-axis_.

The ordered pairs in the table are (1, 22), (2, _0_), (3, _15_), (_4_, 30), and (_5_, 30). These will be the points of the line graph.

Determine a **scale** for each axis. Consider the **range** of values, or how far apart the numbers are, in the set of y-values and the set of x-values.

The numbers on the **x-axis** can increase by _1s_.

The numbers on the **y-axis** can increase by _5s_.

Connect

Label each axis. Number the x-axis by 1s. Number the y-axis by 5s.

Plot each point on the graph. The point (1, 22) means to move right to 1 on the x-axis, move up to 22 on the y-axis, and plot a point.

Then connect the points.

Be sure to include a title for the graph.

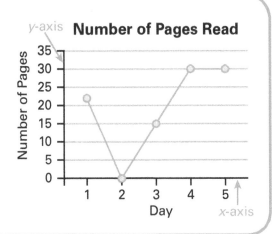

Let's Talk

If the scale on the y-axis increased by 10s instead of 5s, how would the graph look different? Would this affect how you interpreted the graph? Explain why.

Fill in the blanks. Solve the problem.

Every year, the top 2 professional baseball teams compete in the World Series. The winner is the first team to win 4 games. The table lists the number of games played in 5 different years. Create a line graph to display the data.

Year	Number of Games
2002	7
2003	6
2004	4
2005	4
2006	5

■ Show years on the _____ and number of games on the _____.

■ Identify the ordered pairs from the table: (2002, 7), (2003, _____), (2004, _____), (_____, 4), and (_____, 5).

■ Choose a scale. The numbers on the *x*-axis can increase by _____. The numbers on the *y*-axis can increase by _____.

■ Label and number each axis. Plot the points and connect them. Title the graph.

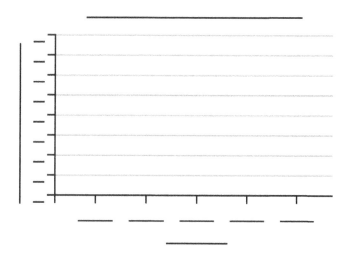

A flat section of a graph shows when the data stay the same.

Your Turn ⟩ **Now, use what you know to solve this problem.**

2. Tia is growing a plant for a science project. She recorded its height on the first day of each month. Complete the line graph to represent Tia's data.

Month	Height (in.)
1	6
2	10
3	18
4	20
5	27

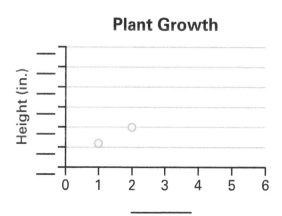

Plant Growth

Solve the problem. Then read why each answer choice is correct or not correct.

Solve

Sarah's bike club went for an all-day ride. The line graph represents her ride.

During which part of the ride did Sarah stop to eat lunch?

Ⓐ between 1 and 2 hours

Ⓑ between 2 and 3 hours

Ⓒ between 3 and 4 hours

Ⓓ between 4 and 5 hours

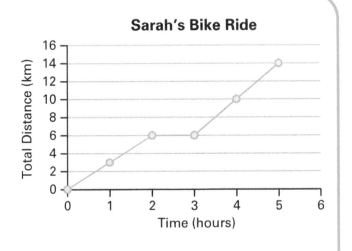

Sarah's Bike Ride

Check

Check to see if you chose the correct answer.

Her distance did not change when she stopped for lunch. The line would be flat when her distance stayed the same. Her distance stayed the same between 2 and 3 hours.

So, the correct answer is Ⓑ.

Why are the other answer choices not correct?

Ⓐ between 1 and 2 hours	The distance increased from 3 km to 6 km. She must have been moving.
Ⓒ between 3 and 4 hours	The distance increased from 6 km to 10 km. She must have been moving.
Ⓓ between 4 and 5 hours	The distance increased from 10 km to 14 km. She must have been moving.

Your Turn ▷ Solve each problem. Use the hints to avoid mistakes.

- Identify the information shown on each axis.
- Determine the ordered pairs of the data points on the graph.
- Find increases and decreases in the data by interpreting the slant of the lines between data points.

Use the line graph below for problems 3–5.

3. The graph represents the value of a company's stock over a period of time. How much greater was the stock price in Month 2 compared to Month 3?

   Ⓐ $5

   Ⓑ $8

   Ⓒ $10

   Ⓓ $18

4. What was the lowest value of the stock during this period of time?

   Ⓐ $2

   Ⓑ $8

   Ⓒ $10

   Ⓓ $16

5. During which month did the stock have its greatest value?

   Ⓐ Month 4

   Ⓑ Month 3

   Ⓒ Month 2

   Ⓓ Month 1

6. Maxwell wants to graph the data shown below.

Week	Snow (cm)
1	6
2	10
3	8
4	2
5	5

   Which scale would be best to use for the y-axis on Maxwell's graph?

   Ⓐ increase by 2s

   Ⓑ increase by 5s

   Ⓒ increase by 10s

   Ⓓ increase by 20s

Study the model. It is a good example of a written answer.

Student Model

Show

Sandy's soccer coach keeps track of the number of goals the team scores each week. Her data are listed in the table. Create a graph to represent the data.

Week	Number of Goals
1	3
2	1
3	0
4	2
5	2

Weeks will be shown on the x-axis. Number of goals will be shown on the y-axis.

The ordered pairs are (1, 3), (2, 1), (3, 0), (4, 2), and (5, 2).

The numbers on the x-axis can increase by 1s. The numbers on the y-axis can increase by 1s.

☑ The student shows each step.

Solution:

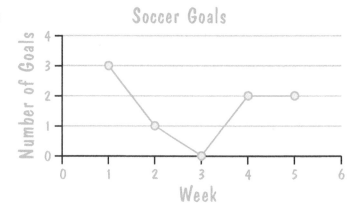

☑ The student correctly creates the line graph.

Explain

Explain how you got your answer.

First, I determined the ordered pairs from the table. Then, I used the range of the data to decide on the scale for the x-axis and the y-axis. I plotted a point for each ordered pair and connected them with line segments. I labeled each axis and wrote a title for the line graph.

☑ The student gives important details about how to create the line graph.

☑ The student uses the math words *range*, *scale*, *x-axis*, *y-axis*, and *line graph*.

7. Delia opened a dance academy in 2006. She made this data table to keep track of the number of students she taught each year. Create a graph to represent the data.

Year	Number of Dancers
2006	30
2007	25
2008	40
2009	40
2010	55

CHECKLIST

Did you . . .

☐ show each step?

☐ correctly create the graph?

☐ give important details?

☐ use math words?

Solution:

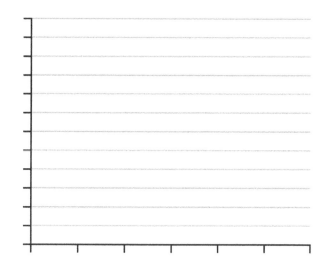

Explain how you got your answer.

_____

_____

_____

_____

As you solve problems involving line graphs, remember to
- make sure you know which quantity is shown on each axis.
- check your graph to make sure it matches your data.

Solve each problem.

Use the line graph for problems 8 and 9.

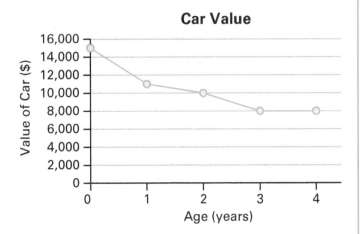

8. Marcus made this graph to show how the value of his car changed as the car got older. During which period of time did his car decrease in value by the greatest amount?

Ⓐ 0 to 1 year

Ⓑ 1 to 2 years

Ⓒ 2 to 3 years

Ⓓ 3 to 4 years

9. What is the final value of the car at the end of 4 years?

Ⓐ $7,000

Ⓑ $8,000

Ⓒ $11,000

Ⓓ $15,000

Use the line graph for problems 10 and 11.

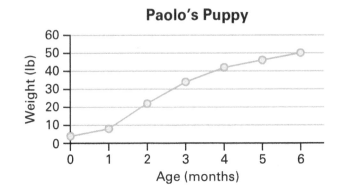

10. Paolo made this graph to show his puppy's weight from birth to age 6 months. Which data for weight did Paolo use to make his graph?

Ⓐ 4, 8, 22, 34, 42, 46, 50

Ⓑ 0, 10, 20, 30, 40, 50, 60

Ⓒ 0, 1, 2, 3, 4, 5, 6

Ⓓ 5, 10, 20, 35, 40, 45, 50

11. What scale did Paolo use for the *y*-axis?

Ⓐ increase by 1s

Ⓑ increase by 5s

Ⓒ increase by 10s

Ⓓ increase by 20s

Data Analysis

Use the table for problems 12–14.

Month	Amount Saved ($)
1	50
2	100
3	150
4	200
5	250

12. Vanessa puts money into her savings account every month. She wants to make a graph to show her total savings. What scale should she use for the *y*-axis?

   Ⓐ increase by 2s   Ⓒ increase by 10s

   Ⓑ increase by 5s   Ⓓ increase by 50s

13. Which ordered pair should be on Vanessa's graph?

   Ⓐ (2, 200)   Ⓒ (3, 50)

   Ⓑ (5, 250)   Ⓓ (1, 10)

14. Complete the graph representing the data from the table.

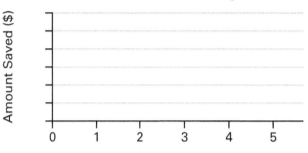

Vanessa's Savings

15. Karl keeps track of the number of instructors he has each year at his karate school. Create a graph to show his data. Then describe the change in the data from Year 2 to Year 3 and from Year 4 to Year 5.

Year	Number of Instructors
1	5
2	16
3	16
4	12
5	15

Solution:

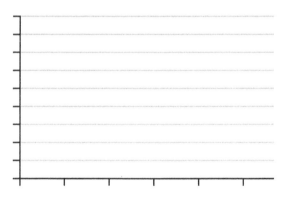

From Year 2 to Year 3, the number of instructors _____.

From Year 4 to Year 5, the number of instructors _____.

Explain how you found your answer.

_____

_____

_____

_____

How can you multiply a whole number by a fraction using repeated addition?

Explore

You can use **multiplication** to find the total amount of equal groups.
One way to multiply whole numbers is to use **repeated addition**.

$$5 \times 3 = ?$$

5 groups of 3

$$3 + 3 + 3 + 3 + 3 = 15$$

How can you multiply if one **factor** is a fraction? $3 \times \dfrac{3}{10}$

Think

Make a model of the problem $3 \times \dfrac{3}{10}$.

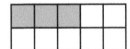 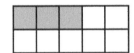 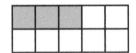

There are ___3___ groups. How much is in each group? $\dfrac{3}{10}$

Connect

To multiply $3 \times \dfrac{3}{10}$, you can use repeated addition to find the **product**.

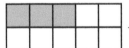 $+$ 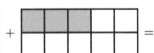 $=$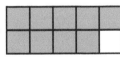

Add: $\dfrac{3}{10} + \dfrac{3}{10} + \dfrac{3}{10} = \dfrac{9}{10}$

3 groups of $\dfrac{3}{10}$ is $\dfrac{9}{10}$.

Let's Talk

Does the order of the factors in a fraction multiplication problem matter? Why or why not?

Fill in the blanks as you solve the problem.

Gabriella and her friends are making 6 fruit smoothies.
One serving of smoothie needs $\frac{2}{3}$ cup of yogurt.

How much yogurt do they need in all?

■ How many smoothies are the friends making? _____

How much yogurt is in each smoothie? _____ cup

■ You can find $6 \times \frac{2}{3}$ using repeated addition.

Think: $6 \times \frac{2}{3}$ means _____ groups of _____.

Add $\frac{2}{3}$ six times. _____ + _____ + _____ + _____ + _____ + _____ = _____

■ You can simplify the answer $\frac{12}{3}$ by dividing.

The numerator 12 divided by the denominator _____ equals _____.

Solution: Gabriella and her friends need _____ cups of yogurt.

> When the **numerator** (top) of a fraction is greater than or equal to the **denominator** (bottom), you have an **improper fraction.** This means the fraction is greater than or equal to one.

Your Turn > Now, use what you know to solve this problem.

1. Use repeated addition to find the product of $4 \times \frac{1}{8}$.

Show your work. Simplify your answer.

$$4 \times \frac{1}{8} = \text{\_\_\_\_\_}$$

PART TWO: Learn More About Multiplying Whole Numbers by Fractions

 How can you multiply a whole number by a fraction without using repeated addition?

Explore

To multiply $8 \times \frac{1}{2}$, you could find the sum shown below.

$$\frac{1}{2} + \frac{1}{2} + \frac{1}{2} + \frac{1}{2} + \frac{1}{2} + \frac{1}{2} + \frac{1}{2} + \frac{1}{2}$$

Is there a quicker way to find the product?

Think

Any whole number can be written as a fraction with a denominator of 1.

$$3 = \frac{3}{1} \qquad\qquad 7 = \frac{7}{1} \qquad\qquad 42 = \frac{42}{1}$$

How can you write the whole number 8 as a fraction? $\dfrac{\boxed{8}}{\boxed{1}}$

Rewrite the multiplication problem $8 \times \frac{1}{2}$ using only fractions. $\dfrac{\boxed{8}}{\boxed{1}} \times \dfrac{\boxed{1}}{\boxed{2}}$

Connect

To multiply two fractions, follow the steps.

Process	Equation
Step 1: Multiply the numerators.	$\frac{8}{1} \times \frac{1}{2} = \frac{8}{}$
Step 2: Multiply the denominators.	$\frac{8}{1} \times \frac{1}{2} = \frac{8}{2}$
Step 3: If possible, simplify your answer.	$\frac{8}{2} = 4$

The product of $8 \times \frac{1}{2} = 4$.

Let's Talk

If you multiply a whole number by 2, the number increases. What happens when you multiply a whole number by $\frac{1}{2}$?

Number and Operations

Fill in the blanks as you solve the problem.

Corine has a ribbon that is 11 feet long. She needs $\frac{2}{3}$ of this ribbon to use for wrapping a gift. How long is the piece of ribbon Corine needs for the gift?

■ You need to find $\frac{2}{3}$ of 11, so multiply $\frac{2}{3} \times 11$.

How can you write the whole number 11 as a fraction? $\frac{\square}{\square}$

Rewrite the multiplication problem $\frac{2}{3} \times 11$ using only fractions.

$$\frac{\square}{\square} \times \frac{\square}{\square}$$

> A fraction bar means division. The number 11 equals $\frac{11}{1}$ because 11 is the same as $11 \div 1$.

■ Multiply the numerators.

$$\frac{2}{3} \times \frac{11}{1} = \frac{\square}{}$$

Multiply the denominators.

$$\frac{2}{3} \times \frac{11}{1} = \frac{22}{\square}$$

■ Simplify the answer by dividing the numerator by the denominator.

$$\frac{22}{3} = 7\frac{\square}{\square}$$

Solution: The piece of ribbon Corine needs for the gift is _____ feet long.

Your Turn **Now, use what you know to solve this problem.**

2. Rewrite $2 \times \frac{3}{4}$ using only fractions.

Then multiply using the steps. Simplify your answer.

$$2 \times \frac{3}{4} = \text{\_\_\_\_}$$

Solve the problem. Then read why each answer choice is correct or not correct.

Solve

Jeff planted 4 rows of tomato seeds in his garden. Each row is $\frac{3}{5}$ foot wide.

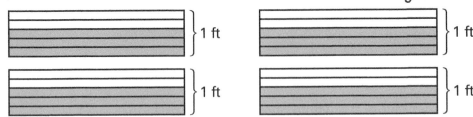

What is the total width of the rows of tomatoes?

Ⓐ $\frac{3}{20}$ ft   Ⓒ $1\frac{2}{5}$ ft

Ⓑ $\frac{12}{20}$ ft   Ⓓ $2\frac{2}{5}$ ft

Check

Check whether you chose the correct answer.

Multiply $4 \times \frac{3}{5}$ to find the total width.

$$4 \times \frac{3}{5} = \frac{4}{1} \times \frac{3}{5} = \frac{12}{5}$$

Simplify the answer.

$$\frac{12}{5} = 2\frac{2}{5}$$

So, the correct answer is Ⓓ.

Why are the other answer choices not correct?

Ⓐ $\frac{3}{20}$ ft	The whole number 4 written as a fraction is $\frac{4}{1}$, not $\frac{1}{4}$.
Ⓑ $\frac{12}{20}$ ft	Multiply 4 by 3 to get the numerator. Multiply 1 by 5, not 4 by 5, to get the denominator.
Ⓒ $1\frac{2}{5}$ ft	There are two groups of 5 in 12, not 1.

- Identify the number of groups and the amount in each group, and then write the problem.
- Solve the problem using repeated addition or multiplication.
- Simplify your answer.

3. Manuel's family ordered 4 different pizzas for dinner. Manuel ate $\frac{1}{6}$ of each pizza. Which equation could **not** be used to find the total amount of the pizza order that Manuel ate?

Ⓐ $\frac{1}{6} + \frac{1}{6} + \frac{1}{6} + \frac{1}{6} = \blacksquare$

Ⓑ $\frac{1}{4} + \frac{1}{4} + \frac{1}{4} + \frac{1}{4} + \frac{1}{4} + \frac{1}{4} = \blacksquare$

Ⓒ $4 \times \frac{1}{6} = \blacksquare$

Ⓓ $\frac{1}{6} \times 4 = \blacksquare$

4. Which two expressions have the same result?

Ⓐ $\frac{2}{3} + \frac{2}{3} + \frac{2}{3}; \ 2 \times \frac{2}{3}$

Ⓑ $2 \times \frac{3}{2}; \ 2 \times \frac{2}{3}$

Ⓒ $2 \times \frac{2}{3}; \ \frac{2}{3} \times 3$

Ⓓ $\frac{2}{3} + \frac{2}{3} + \frac{2}{3}; \ \frac{2}{3} \times 3$

5. Jin is building a spaceship with snap-together blocks. Each block is $\frac{5}{8}$ inch wide. If the widest part of the ship has 10 blocks side by side, how many inches wide is that part of Jin's spaceship?

Ⓐ $\frac{5}{80}$ in. Ⓒ $6\frac{1}{4}$ in.

Ⓑ $\frac{1}{16}$ in. Ⓓ $10\frac{5}{8}$ in.

6. Janeka bought a 5-pound bag of flour. She used $\frac{11}{15}$ of the flour for muffins.

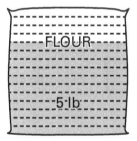

How many pounds of flour did Janeka use to make the muffins?

Ⓐ $1\frac{1}{15}$ lb Ⓒ $4\frac{2}{3}$ lb

Ⓑ $3\frac{2}{3}$ lb Ⓓ $5\frac{11}{15}$ lb

Study the model. It is a good example of a written answer.

Student Model

Show

Dominique's friend is lending her 2 of her favorite music CDs. Each CD, in its case, is $\frac{3}{8}$ inch tall. How tall are the two CDs stacked on top of each other?

Show your work and simplify your answer. Then explain how you found the solution.

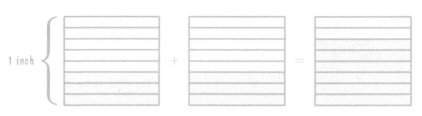

Multiply $2 \times \frac{3}{8}$.

$2 \times \frac{3}{8} = \frac{2}{1} \times \frac{3}{8} = \frac{6}{8}$

Simplify the answer.

$\frac{6 \div 2}{8 \div 2} = \frac{3}{4}$

The two CDs are $\frac{3}{4}$ inch thick.

Solution: _____

☑ The student shows each step.

☑ The student correctly answers the question asked.

Explain

Explanation:

There are 2 CDs that are each $\frac{3}{8}$ inch. I drew a picture to

help me see the problem. Then I multiplied 2 times $\frac{3}{8}$.

I wrote 2 as $\frac{2}{1}$ and then multiplied $\frac{2}{1}$ by $\frac{3}{8}$ to get $\frac{6}{8}$.

I simplified my answer by dividing the numerator and

denominator by 2, getting the final answer of $\frac{3}{4}$ inch.

☑ The student gives important details about how to find the height.

☑ The student uses the math words *multiply*, *numerator*, *denominator*, and *simplify*.

7. Rachel has 6 classes every school day. Each class is $\frac{3}{4}$ hour long. How much time does Rachel spend in class during the school day?

Show your work and simplify your answer. Then explain how you found the solution.

CHECKLIST

Did you . . .

☐ show each step?

☐ answer the question asked?

☐ give important details?

☐ use math words?

Solution: _____

Explanation:

_____

_____

_____

_____

When you multiply whole numbers by fractions, remember to
- draw pictures to show equal groups and then multiply.
- simplify your answer.
- use repeated addition to check your work.

Solve each problem.

8. Which equation **cannot** be used to find the total of the shaded areas?

- (A) $\frac{1}{3} \times 5 = \blacksquare$
- (B) $5 \times \frac{1}{3} = \blacksquare$
- (C) $\frac{1}{5} + \frac{1}{5} + \frac{1}{5} = \blacksquare$
- (D) $\frac{1}{3} + \frac{1}{3} + \frac{1}{3} + \frac{1}{3} + \frac{1}{3} = \blacksquare$

9. Which expression is the same as $2 \times \frac{5}{6}$?

- (A) $\frac{5}{6} + \frac{5}{6}$
- (B) $\frac{2}{1} + \frac{2}{1} + \frac{2}{1} + \frac{2}{1} + \frac{2}{1}$
- (C) $\frac{2}{5} + \frac{2}{5} + \frac{2}{5} + \frac{2}{5} + \frac{2}{5} + \frac{2}{5}$
- (D) $\frac{1}{2} + \frac{1}{2} + \frac{1}{2} + \frac{1}{2} + \frac{1}{2} + \frac{1}{2}$

10. Finn's uncle is cutting boards for a hardwood floor. Each board is $\frac{1}{4}$ foot wide. For one part of the floor, he needs 8 boards. How many feet wide is that part of the floor?

- (A) $\frac{1}{32}$ ft
- (B) $\frac{1}{2}$ ft
- (C) 2 ft
- (D) 32 ft

11. What is the product of 4 and $\frac{9}{10}$?

- (A) $\frac{9}{40}$
- (B) $\frac{9}{10}$
- (C) $3\frac{3}{4}$
- (D) $3\frac{3}{5}$

12. Ava planted a flower bulb in a pot. The flower grew $\frac{4}{5}$ inch each week during 6 weeks in the spring. How many inches did Ava's flower grow during those weeks?

Ⓐ $\frac{2}{15}$ in.　　Ⓒ 2 in.

Ⓑ $1\frac{2}{3}$ in.　　Ⓓ $4\frac{4}{5}$ in.

13. Solve. $9 \times \frac{2}{3} = $ ▨

Ⓐ $\frac{2}{27}$　　Ⓒ $3\frac{2}{3}$

Ⓑ $\frac{1}{6}$　　Ⓓ 6

14. Lacy's hair grows $\frac{2}{5}$ inch every month. She let it grow for 3 months between haircuts. How many inches did Lacy's hair grow in that time?

Write an addition equation and a multiplication equation that show the amount of hair growth.

Addition equation:

_____

Multiplication equation:

_____

15. Benjamin and his friends are making homemade slime. The recipe needs $\frac{3}{4}$ cup glue for each batch of slime. If Benjamin plans to make 7 batches of slime, how much glue does he need?

Show your work and simplify your answer. Then explain how you found the solution.

Solution: _____

Explanation:

_____

_____

_____

_____

How can you use a model to multiply a fraction by a fraction?

Explore

You can use repeated addition to **multiply** a whole number by a **fraction**.

$$3 \times \frac{2}{3} = \frac{2}{3} + \frac{2}{3} + \frac{2}{3}$$

3 groups of $\frac{2}{3}$

How can you use a model to multiply a fraction by a fraction? $\frac{1}{2} \times \frac{2}{3}$

Think

$\frac{1}{2} \times \frac{2}{3}$ means $\underline{\frac{1}{2}}$ of $\underline{\frac{2}{3}}$. Shade the model to show $\frac{2}{3}$.

$\frac{1}{3}$	$\frac{1}{3}$	$\frac{1}{3}$

There are $\underline{\quad 3 \quad}$ thirds in all, and $\underline{\quad 2 \quad}$ should be shaded.

Connect

Show $\frac{1}{2}$ of $\frac{2}{3}$ on the model.

Divide each third into two halves. The model is now divided into sixths. Shade $\frac{1}{2}$ of each shaded third.

Two of the sixths, or $\frac{2}{6}$, are double-shaded. So, $\frac{1}{2}$ of $\frac{2}{3}$ is $\frac{2}{6}$, or $\frac{1}{2} \times \frac{2}{3} = \frac{2}{6}$.

The model shows that you can multiply the **numerators** and multiply the **denominators** to find the **product**.

$$\frac{1}{2} \times \frac{2}{3} = \frac{1 \times 2}{2 \times 3} = \frac{2}{6}$$

Let's Talk

Give an example of a real-life situation involving a fraction times a fraction. Think of a situation when you need to find "a fraction *of* a fraction."

Fill in the blanks as you solve the problem.

At Jacob's school, $\frac{1}{4}$ of the students play an instrument in the band. Two-thirds of those band students play a woodwind instrument. What fraction of all the students in his school play a woodwind?

■ You need to find _____ of _____.

First, shade the model to show $\frac{1}{4}$.

There are _____ fourths in all, and _____ should be shaded.

■ Now, show $\frac{2}{3}$ of $\frac{1}{4}$ on the model.

Divide each fourth into _____ thirds.

Then shade _____ of the shaded fourth.

The double-shaded portion shows _____ of the whole.

■ So, $\frac{2}{3} \times \frac{1}{4} = \dfrac{\boxed{}}{\boxed{}} = $ _____.

■ Simplify the answer by dividing the numerator and denominator by their greatest common factor, 2.

$\dfrac{}{} = \dfrac{}{}$

Solution: _____ of all the students play a woodwind instrument.

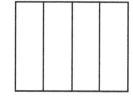

When using a model for fraction multiplication, shade the second fraction first.

Your Turn Now, use what you know to solve this problem.

1. Solve. $\frac{4}{5} \times \frac{1}{2}$

Use the model to find the product. Simplify your answer.

$\frac{4}{5} \times \frac{1}{2} = \dfrac{\boxed{}}{\boxed{}} = \dfrac{}{} = \dfrac{}{}$

How can you multiply a fraction by a mixed number?

Explore

To multiply a fraction by a fraction, you can multiply the numerators and multiply the denominators to find the product.

$$\frac{3}{5} \times \frac{1}{4} = \frac{3 \times 1}{5 \times 4} = \frac{3}{20}$$

How can you multiply a fraction by a **mixed number**? $\frac{3}{5} \times 3\frac{1}{3}$

Think

Find ___$\frac{3}{5}$___ of ___$3\frac{1}{3}$___.

Write the mixed number $3\frac{1}{3}$ as an **improper fraction**. Three wholes, each divided into thirds, equal ___9___ thirds, plus 1 third equal ___10___ thirds. $3\frac{1}{3} = \frac{\boxed{10}}{\boxed{3}}$

Rewrite the problem $\frac{3}{5} \times 3\frac{1}{3}$ using only fractions: $\frac{\boxed{3}}{\boxed{5}} \times \frac{\boxed{10}}{\boxed{3}}$

Connect

Follow the steps to multiply.

Step 1: **Cross-simplify** if possible. Use the **greatest common factor** (GCF).	$\overset{1}{\underset{1}{\frac{3}{5}}} \times \overset{2}{\underset{1}{\frac{10}{3}}}$ Divide 3 and 3 by the GCF 3. Divide 10 and 5 by the GCF 5.
Step 2: Multiply the numerators.	$\frac{1}{1} \times \frac{2}{1} = \frac{1 \times 2}{\rule{1cm}{0.4pt}} = \frac{2}{\rule{0.5cm}{0.4pt}}$
Step 3: Multiply the denominators.	$\frac{1}{1} \times \frac{2}{1} = \frac{1 \times 2}{1 \times 1} = \frac{2}{1}$
Step 4: If possible, simplify the answer.	$\frac{2}{1} = 2$

So $\frac{3}{5} \times 3\frac{1}{3} = 2$.

Let's Talk

Explain why it is helpful to cross-simplify before multiplying.

Fill in the blanks as you solve the problem.

Students ate pizza at an end-of-year class picnic. Afterward, there were still $4\frac{1}{3}$ pizzas left. The teachers ate $\frac{3}{4}$ of the remaining pizza. How many pizzas did the teachers eat?

■ You need to find _____ of _____.

Write $4\frac{1}{3}$ as an improper fraction. Four wholes equals _____ thirds, plus one third equals _____ thirds: $\frac{\square}{\square}$.

How can the problem $\frac{3}{4} \times 4\frac{1}{3}$ be written using only fractions?

$\frac{\square}{\square} \times \frac{\square}{\square}$

■ Multiply the fractions using the steps.

1. Cross-simplify if possible. $\frac{\square}{}\frac{3}{4} \times \frac{13}{3}\frac{}{\square}$

2. Multiply the numerators. $\frac{1}{4} \times \frac{13}{1} = \frac{\square \times \square}{} = \frac{\square}{}$

3. Multiply the denominators. $\frac{1}{4} \times \frac{13}{1} = \frac{1 \times 13}{\square \times \square} = \frac{13}{\square}$

4. If possible, simplify the answer. $\frac{13}{4} = \square\frac{\square}{\square}$

Solution: The teachers ate _____ pizzas.

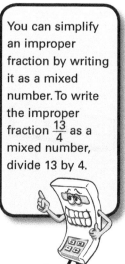

You can simplify an improper fraction by writing it as a mixed number. To write the improper fraction $\frac{13}{4}$ as a mixed number, divide 13 by 4.

Your Turn

Now, use what you know to solve this problem.

2. Rewrite $\frac{5}{6} \times 1\frac{7}{10}$ using only fractions. Then multiply using the steps. Simplify the answer.

$$\frac{5}{6} \times 1\frac{7}{10} = \underline{\quad\quad}$$

Solve the problem. Then read why each answer choice is correct or not correct.

Solve

Milo has a collection of music CDs. Three-fourths of them are albums by solo artists. Of those solo artists, $\frac{2}{9}$ are female.

What portion of Milo's CD collection is music by female solo artists?

Ⓐ $\frac{1}{6}$

Ⓑ $\frac{1}{5}$

Ⓒ $\frac{2}{5}$

Ⓓ $\frac{2}{3}$

Check

Check whether you chose the correct answer.

You can find $\frac{2}{9}$ of $\frac{3}{4}$ using the fraction multiplication steps.

Step 1: Cross-simplify.

Step 2: Multiply numerators.

Step 3: Multiply denominators.

$$\frac{^{1}\cancel{2}}{_{3}\cancel{9}} \times \frac{\cancel{3}^{1}}{\cancel{4}_{2}} = \frac{1 \times 1}{3 \times 2} = \frac{1}{6}$$

The answer is already in simplest form.

So, the correct answer is Ⓐ.

Why are the other answer choices not correct?

Ⓑ	$\frac{1}{5}$	After cross-simplifying, multiply the numerators and multiply the denominators.
Ⓒ	$\frac{2}{5}$	After cross-simplifying, multiply the numerators and multiply the denominators.
Ⓓ	$\frac{2}{3}$	Three-fourths does not equal $3\frac{1}{4}$.

Your Turn — Solve each problem. Use the hints to avoid mistakes.

- Look for fractions that are written as words.
- Write the word "of" as "×" in a multiplication problem.
- Write mixed numbers as improper fractions before multiplying.
- Use cross-simplifying when possible.
- Multiply numerators and multiply denominators.

3. Which math sentence can be used to find five-sixths of $3\frac{1}{8}$?

   Ⓐ $\frac{5}{6} + 3\frac{1}{8} = \blacksquare$

   Ⓑ $3\frac{1}{8} - \frac{5}{6} = \blacksquare$

   Ⓒ $5\frac{1}{6} \times 3\frac{1}{8} = \blacksquare$

   Ⓓ $\frac{5}{6} \times 3\frac{1}{8} = \blacksquare$

4. Which fraction multiplication problem does this model show?

   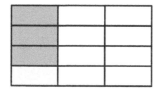

   Ⓐ $\frac{3}{12} \times \frac{1}{12}$

   Ⓑ $\frac{1}{12} \times \frac{1}{3}$

   Ⓒ $\frac{3}{4} \times \frac{1}{3}$

   Ⓓ $\frac{1}{4} \times \frac{3}{4}$

5. Shawnita is making macaroni and cheese for her little brother. The recipe calls for $\frac{3}{4}$ cup of milk. If she is only making one-third of the recipe, how much milk should Shawnita use?

   Ⓐ $\frac{1}{4}$ cup

   Ⓑ $\frac{2}{5}$ cup

   Ⓒ $\frac{4}{7}$ cup

   Ⓓ 1 cup

6. Find the product.

   $$\frac{2}{3} \times 4\frac{1}{2} = \blacksquare$$

   Ⓐ 2

   Ⓑ 3

   Ⓒ $2\frac{1}{5}$

   Ⓓ $4\frac{1}{3}$

Study the model. It is a good example of a written answer.

Student Model

Show

The directions for a bottle of fish tank cleaner say to use $3\frac{1}{3}$ teaspoons for a 50-gallon tank. Since Raya's fish tank is only 10 gallons, she needs to use $\frac{1}{5}$ of the indicated amount of cleaner. How much fish tank cleaner should Raya use?

Show your work and simplify your answer.

Then explain how you found the solution.

$$\frac{1}{5} \text{ of } 3\frac{1}{3} \text{ is the same as } \frac{1}{5} \times 3\frac{1}{3}.$$

$$\frac{1}{5} \times 3\frac{1}{3} = \frac{1}{\overset{1}{5}} \times \frac{\overset{2}{10}}{3} = \frac{1 \times 2}{1 \times 3} = \frac{2}{3}$$

> ☑ The student shows each step.

Solution: Raya should use $\frac{2}{3}$ teaspoon of the fish tank cleaner.

> ☑ The student correctly answers the question asked.

Explain

Explanation:

Raya needs to use $\frac{1}{5}$ of the indicated $3\frac{1}{3}$ teaspoons of cleaner. So I wrote this as a multiplication problem, with the word "of" changed to "×". Before multiplying, I rewrote the mixed number $3\frac{1}{3}$ as the improper fraction $\frac{10}{3}$. Then I cross-simplified by dividing both the denominator 5 and the numerator 10 by 5. When I multiplied the numerators and multiplied the denominators, I got the answer $\frac{2}{3}$, which did not need to be simplified any further.

> ☑ The student gives important details about how the amount of cleaner was found.

> ☑ The student uses the math words *multiply*, *mixed number*, *improper fraction*, and *cross-simplify*.

7. Nikos spent $5\frac{1}{5}$ hours this week playing different video games. One-half of that time was spent on his favorite game, "Star Commands."

How many hours did Nikos play "Star Commands" this week?

Show your work and simplify your answer. Then explain how you found the solution.

CHECKLIST

Did you . . .

☐ show each step?

☐ answer the question asked?

☐ give important details?

☐ use math words?

Solution: _____

Explanation:

_____

_____

_____

_____

_____

_____

As you multiply fractions by fractions and mixed numbers, you may want to

- use models to find double-shaded regions of fractions multiplied by fractions.
- use multiplication steps with cross-simplifying.

Solve each problem.

8. Which model shows $\frac{2}{5}$ of $\frac{3}{4}$?

9. Which expression is the same as $\frac{7}{8}$ of $2\frac{5}{6}$?

Ⓐ $\frac{7}{8} + 2\frac{5}{6}$

Ⓑ $\frac{7}{8} \times \frac{17}{6}$

Ⓒ $\frac{7}{8} \times \frac{5}{6} + 2$

Ⓓ $\frac{14}{8} \times \frac{5}{6}$

10. A recipe calls for $2\frac{1}{4}$ cups of flour. If Huang needs to cut the recipe in half, how many cups of flour should he use?

Ⓐ $1\frac{1}{8}$ cups

Ⓑ $1\frac{1}{4}$ cups

Ⓒ $2\frac{1}{8}$ cups

Ⓓ $4\frac{1}{2}$ cups

11. Stanley poured $\frac{3}{10}$ of a pitcher of juice into a glass. He drank $\frac{5}{7}$ of the juice in the glass. How much of the pitcher did he drink?

Ⓐ $\frac{3}{35}$

Ⓑ $\frac{3}{14}$

Ⓒ $\frac{4}{9}$

Ⓓ $\frac{1}{3}$

12. While playing a word game, $\frac{1}{4}$ of the letter tiles Lucia got were vowels. Of those vowels, $\frac{1}{3}$ were the letter E. What portion of Lucia's tiles was the letter E?

Ⓐ $\frac{1}{12}$ Ⓒ $\frac{1}{6}$

Ⓑ $\frac{1}{7}$ Ⓓ $\frac{2}{7}$

13. What is the product of $\frac{3}{8} \times 1\frac{1}{6}$?

Ⓐ $\frac{7}{16}$ Ⓒ $1\frac{1}{16}$

Ⓑ $\frac{1}{2}$ Ⓓ $1\frac{3}{4}$

14. What is $\frac{3}{4}$ of $\frac{1}{2}$?

Show the answer to this problem using a model and using multiplication steps.

Model:

_____

Multiplication:

_____

15. Garrett spent $6\frac{3}{4}$ hours on homework last week. Four-ninths of that homework time was spent on a history report. How much time did Garrett work on his history report last week?

Show your work and simplify your answer. Then explain how you found the solution.

Solution: _____

Explanation:

_____

_____

_____

_____

 **How can you divide a whole number by a unit fraction?**

Explore

A **fraction** shows a part of a whole.

A **unit fraction** is a fraction with a numerator of 1, such as $\frac{1}{3}$.

How can you divide a whole number by a unit fraction?

$$2 \div \frac{1}{3}$$

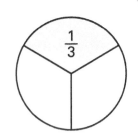

Think

The problem asks you to find how many ___thirds___ are in ___2___ wholes.

Model the **dividend**, or the number being divided.

There are ___2___ wholes.

Model the **divisor**, or the number to divide by.

Divide each whole into ___3___ equal parts.

Connect

Divide each rectangle in thirds. Label each third.
Count the number of thirds in all.

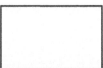

There are 6 thirds in all.

So, $2 \div \frac{1}{3} = 6$.

Let's Talk

Why is the quotient of $2 \div \frac{1}{3}$ greater than 2?

Fill in the blanks as you solve the problem.

Sophie has 5 yards of ribbon. She uses $\frac{1}{4}$ yard of ribbon to make each bow.

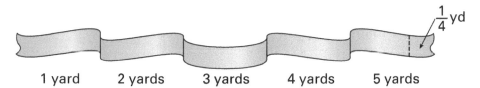

$\frac{1}{4}$ yd

1 yard   2 yards   3 yards   4 yards   5 yards

How many bows can she make?

■ The problem asks you to find how many _____ yard pieces are in _____ whole yards.

The picture models the dividend. There are _____ wholes.

Use the picture to model the divisor. Each whole should be divided into _____ equal parts.

■ In the picture, divide each yard of ribbon in _____.

Count the number of fourths in all.
There are _____ fourths in all.

■ So, $5 \div \frac{1}{4} =$ _____.

Solution: Sophie can make _____ bows.

> The result of dividing numbers is the **quotient**.

Your Turn

Now, use what you know to solve this problem.

1. Use the model to find the quotient of $4 \div \frac{1}{6}$.

$4 \div \frac{1}{6} =$ _____

 How can you divide a whole number by a fraction?

Explore

You can use models to help you divide whole numbers by fractions.

$2 \div \dfrac{2}{5}$ — How many groups of $\dfrac{2}{5}$ are in 2 wholes?

Draw 2 wholes, each divided into fifths. Find how many groups of $\dfrac{2}{5}$ are in 2.

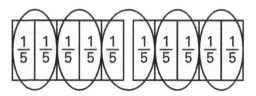   There are 5 groups.

How can you divide without using models?

Think

Find how many groups of $\underline{\dfrac{2}{5}}$ are in $\underline{2}$ wholes.　　　　$2 \div \dfrac{2}{5}$

Rewrite the whole number as a fraction:　　　　　$2 = \dfrac{\boxed{2}}{\boxed{1}}$

Rewrite the problem using only fractions:　　　　$\dfrac{\boxed{2}}{\boxed{1}} \div \dfrac{\boxed{2}}{\boxed{5}}$

What is the **reciprocal**, or multiplicative inverse, of $\dfrac{2}{5}$?　$\dfrac{\boxed{5}}{\boxed{2}}$

Connect

Dividing by a fraction is the same as multiplying by the fraction's reciprocal. To divide:

1. Rewrite the division problem as a multiplication problem. Multiply the dividend by the reciprocal of the divisor.

3. Simplify.

$$\dfrac{2}{1} \div \dfrac{2}{5} = \dfrac{2}{1} \times \dfrac{5}{2} = \dfrac{2 \times 5}{1 \times 2} = \dfrac{10}{2} = 5$$

2. Multiply **numerators**. Multiply **denominators**.

So, $2 \div \dfrac{2}{5} = 5$.

Let's Talk

How can you check the answer to the division problem above? Use your method to check it.

Fill in the blanks as you solve the problem.

Miguel had a pizza party. Each person at the party ate $\frac{2}{3}$ of a pizza.

There were no leftovers. Miguel served a total of 6 small pizzas.

How many people were at the party?

■ Find how many groups of _____ are in _____ wholes.

Rewrite the whole number as a fraction. $6 = \dfrac{\square}{\square}$

■ Rewrite the problem using only fractions. $\dfrac{\square}{\square} \div \dfrac{\square}{\square}$

What is the **reciprocal**, or multiplicative inverse of $\frac{2}{3}$? $\dfrac{\square}{\square}$

> Any whole number can be written as a fraction with a denominator of 1. $4 = \dfrac{4}{1}$

■ Rewrite the division problem as a multiplication problem. Use the reciprocal.

$$\frac{6}{1} \div \frac{2}{3} = \frac{\square}{\square} \times \frac{\square}{\square}$$

■ Multiply the numerators. Multiply the denominators. Simplify the answer.

$$\frac{6}{1} \times \frac{3}{2} = \frac{\square}{\square} = \boxed{}$$

Solution: There were _____ people at the party.

Your Turn ▷ **Now, use what you know to solve this problem.**

2. Rewrite $5 \div \frac{3}{4}$ as a multiplication problem.

Find the quotient using the steps. Simplify your answer.

$$5 \div \frac{3}{4} = \underline{}$$

Solve the problem. Then read why each answer choice is correct or not correct.

Solve

Charlie bought a box of cereal. There are 6 cups of cereal in the box.

The nutrition label gives the serving size as $\frac{3}{4}$ cup.

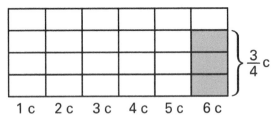

How many servings of cereal are in the box?

Ⓐ 24 servings

Ⓑ $6\frac{3}{4}$ servings

Ⓒ   8 servings

Ⓓ $4\frac{1}{2}$ servings

Check

Check whether you chose the correct answer.

Divide $6 \div \frac{3}{4}$ to find the number of servings.

Rewrite $6 \div \frac{3}{4}$ as a multiplication problem. Then solve.

$$6 \div \frac{3}{4} = \frac{6}{1} \times \frac{4}{3} = \frac{24}{3} = 8$$

So, the correct answer is Ⓒ.

Why are the other answer choices not correct?

Ⓐ 24 servings	This is the product of the numerators only.
Ⓑ $6\frac{3}{4}$ servings	The division problem $6 \div \frac{3}{4}$ is not the same as $6\frac{3}{4}$.
Ⓓ $4\frac{1}{2}$ servings	This is the product of $6 \times \frac{3}{4}$. Use the reciprocal $\frac{4}{3}$.

- Identify the groups and the number of wholes in the problem.
- Solve it using a model or division.
- Use the reciprocal of the divisor when rewriting the problem as a multiplication sentence.

3. Bailey has a recipe for banana pudding. The recipe makes 4 cups of pudding. She pours $\frac{1}{2}$ cup of pudding into each bowl.

1 cup   1 cup

1 cup   1 cup

How many bowls does Bailey need?

Ⓐ 9

Ⓑ 8

Ⓒ 4

Ⓓ 2

4. Which expression is the same as $7 \div \frac{3}{8}$?

Ⓐ $\frac{1}{7} \times \frac{3}{8}$

Ⓑ $\frac{1}{7} \times \frac{8}{3}$

Ⓒ $\frac{7}{1} \times \frac{3}{8}$

Ⓓ $\frac{7}{1} \times \frac{8}{3}$

5. Cho's grandfather enjoys gardening and has many potted plants on his back porch. Each year he changes the soil in each pot. He bought 10 bags of potting soil and uses $\frac{2}{3}$ of a bag for each pot. How many pots can Cho's grandfather fill with soil?

Ⓐ 30

Ⓑ 20

Ⓒ 15

Ⓓ 10

6. What is the quotient of $6 \div \frac{4}{5}$?

Ⓐ 30

Ⓑ $7\frac{1}{2}$

Ⓒ $4\frac{4}{5}$

Ⓓ $\frac{2}{15}$

Study the model. It is a good example of a written answer.

Student Model

Show

Malakai has 4 cups of flour. He uses $\frac{2}{3}$ cup of flour for each mini-loaf of bread he makes. How many loaves can Malakai make?

Show each step. Then explain how you found the solution.

$$4 \div \frac{2}{3} = \frac{4}{1} \div \frac{2}{3} = \frac{4}{1} \times \frac{3}{2} = \frac{12}{2} = 6$$

Check. $6 \times \frac{2}{3} = \frac{6}{1} \times \frac{2}{3} = \frac{12}{3} = 4$

☑ The student shows each step.

Solution: _____ 6 loaves _____

☑ The student correctly answers the question asked.

Explanation:

Malakai has 4 cups. He needs $\frac{2}{3}$ cup for each loaf. I need

to find how many two-thirds are in 4. I can divide to find

the answer. Dividing by a fraction is the same as

multiplying by its reciprocal. So, I rewrote $4 \div \frac{2}{3}$ as

$\frac{4}{1} \times \frac{3}{2}$. Then, I multiplied the numerators and multiplied

the denominators. The answer was an improper fraction,

so I simplified it, $\frac{12}{2} = 6$. To check my answer, I

multiplied the quotient by the divisor, $6 \times \frac{2}{3} = \frac{12}{3} = 4$.

The product is equal to the dividend, so the answer

is correct.

☑ The student gives important details about how the number of loaves was found.

☑ The student uses the math words *reciprocal*, *numerators*, *divide*, *fraction*, *denominators*, *quotient*, and *simplify*.

7. Mr. Reed is building shelves for his workshop. He has a piece of wood that is 3 meters long. He wants to make each shelf $\frac{3}{5}$ meter long. How many shelves can Mr. Reed cut from his piece of wood?

Show each step. Then explain how you found the solution.

> ☑ **CHECKLIST**
>
> Did you . . .
>
> ☐ show each step?
>
> ☐ answer the question asked?
>
> ☐ give important details?
>
> ☐ use math words?

Solution: _____

Explanation:

_____

_____

_____

_____

_____

As you divide whole numbers by fractions, you may want to
- draw pictures to find how many fractional parts are in the wholes.
- write each step as you solve the problems.
- use multiplication to check your work.

Solve each problem.

8. A landscaper places stepping-stones in a park to make a walking path. The path is 7 yards long. Each stepping-stone is $\frac{1}{3}$ yard long.

$\frac{1}{3}$ yd

1 yd 2 yd 3 yd 4 yd 5 yd 6 yd 7 yd

How many stepping stones does the landscaper use to make the path?

Ⓐ $2\frac{1}{3}$

Ⓑ $7\frac{1}{3}$

Ⓒ 7

Ⓓ 21

9. What is the quotient of $3 \div \frac{1}{2}$?

Ⓐ 6

Ⓑ 3

Ⓒ $1\frac{1}{2}$

Ⓓ $\frac{1}{6}$

10. Heidi's father built a ladder for her tree house. The ladder is 8 feet high. The space between each step is $\frac{4}{5}$ feet. How many steps are on the ladder?

Ⓐ 40

Ⓑ 32

Ⓒ 10

Ⓓ 6

11. Sanaa bought a 9-cup bag of cat food. She feeds her cat $\frac{3}{4}$ cup of food a day. How many days until Sanaa must buy more cat food?

Ⓐ 36

Ⓑ 27

Ⓒ 12

Ⓓ 6

12. How many $\frac{1}{4}$ hours are in 5 hours?

Ⓐ   1

Ⓑ   2

Ⓒ   9

Ⓓ   20

13. Which expression is the same as $9 \div \frac{2}{3}$?

Ⓐ $\frac{2}{27}$

Ⓑ   6

Ⓒ $13\frac{1}{2}$

Ⓓ   27

14. For dessert, Tamara served blueberry parfaits. She put $\frac{3}{8}$ cup of blueberries in each bowl. She used a total of 3 cups of blueberries. How many bowls did she fill?

Write a division problem and solve to show the number of bowls.

Division problem:

_____

Solution:

_____

15. Reece works at a bakery. Today he is baking carrot nut muffins. The recipe calls for $\frac{3}{4}$ cup of chopped walnuts for each batch. Reece has a total of 6 cups of walnuts. How many batches of carrot muffins can Reece bake?

Show each step. Then explain how you found the solution.

Solution: _____

Explanation:

_____

_____

_____

_____

_____

 How can you multiply decimal numbers by powers of ten?

Explore

A **power of ten** means 10 raised to some power.
Some powers of ten include 10, 100, and 1,000.

$10^1 = 10$

$10^2 = 100$

$10^3 = 1,000$

How can you multiply **decimal numbers** by powers of ten?

Think

Study the chart. It shows 0.48 multiplied by powers of ten. Look for patterns in the equations. Then complete the statements.

$0.48 \times 10 = 4.8$	The decimal point moved ___1___ place to the right.
$0.48 \times 100 = 48$	The decimal point moved ___2___ places to the right.
$0.48 \times 1,000 = 480$	The decimal point moved ___3___ places to the right.

Does multiplying a decimal number by a power of ten
increase or decrease the number? ___increase___

Connect

Move the **decimal point** to the right when you multiply by a power of ten.

To multiply a decimal by 10, move the decimal point 1 place to the right: 0.48×10 $0.48 \rightarrow 4.8$	Then fill any "empty" space with a zero to show that place value.
To multiply a decimal by 100, move the decimal point 2 places to the right: 0.48×100 $0.48 \rightarrow 48$	
To multiply a decimal by 1,000, move the decimal point 3 places to the right: $0.48 \times 1,000$ $0.48 \rightarrow 480$	

Let's Talk

Is the **product** of 5.6×100 greater than or less than 5? How do you know?

Fill in the blanks as you solve the problem.

Mark is looking at an organism under a microscope.
The organism is 0.25 millimeters long.
The microscope magnifies the organism 100 times.

Magnification: 100×

How big does the organism look under the microscope?

■ Find 0.25 × 100 = ▨.

■ Does multiplying by a power of ten increase or decrease the number? _____

■ To multiply by 100, move the decimal point _____ places to the _____.

■ Multiply.

0.25 × 100 = _____

Solution: The organism looks _____ millimeters long under the microscope.

> An **exponent** tells how many times the **base** is used as a factor. For powers of ten, the exponent equals the number of zeros.
>
> $10^1 = 10 \times 1$
> $\qquad = 10$
>
> $10^2 = 10 \times 10$
> $\qquad = 100$
>
> $10^3 = 10 \times 10 \times 10$
> $\qquad = 1,000$

Your Turn **Now, use what you know to solve this problem.**

1. A ladybug measures 0.375 inches long. How long does the ladybug look under a microscope that magnifies 1,000 times? Show your work.

_____ × _____ = _____

How can you divide decimal numbers by powers of ten?

Explore

Multiplying a decimal number by a power of ten increases the number. The decimal point is moved to the right.

$$89.2 \times 10 = 892$$

How can you divide decimal numbers by powers of ten?

Think

Study the chart. It shows 89.2 divided by powers of 10. Look for patterns in the equations. Then complete the statements.

$89.2 \div 10 = 8.92$	The decimal point moved ___1___ place to the left.
$89.2 \div 100 = 0.892$	The decimal point moved ___2___ places to the left.
$89.2 \div 1,000 = 0.0892$	The decimal point moved ___3___ places to the left.

Does dividing a decimal number by a power of ten increase or decrease the number? ___decrease___

Connect

Move the decimal point to the left when you divide by a power of ten.

To divide a decimal by 10, move the decimal point 1 place to the left: $89.2 \div 10$ $\qquad$ $89.2 \rightarrow 8.92$	Then fill any "empty" space with a zero to show that place value.
To divide a decimal by 100, move the decimal point 2 places to the left: $89.2 \div 100$ $\qquad$ $89.2 \rightarrow 0.892$	
To divide a decimal by 1,000, move the decimal point 3 places to the left: $89.2 \div 1000$ $\qquad$ $89.2 \rightarrow 0.0892$	

Let's Talk

How can you determine which power of ten is used in the following equation?

$$3.75 \div \blacksquare = 0.0375$$

Fill in the blanks as you solve the problem.

Mr. Engles has 174.5 pounds of clay for his pottery class.
He divides the clay evenly among 100 students.

How much clay does each student get?

■ Find $174.5 \div 100 =$ ▢.

■ Does dividing by a power of ten increase or decrease the number?

_____

■ To divide by 100, move the decimal point _____ places to the _____.

■ Divide.

$174.5 \div 100 =$ _____

Solution: Each student gets _____ pounds of clay.

> Place a zero before the decimal point for decimal numbers less than one. For example:
>
> 0.125

Your Turn　**Now, use what you know to solve this problem.**

2. A box of paper clips weighs 0.95 pounds.
    There are 1,000 paper clips in the box.
    What is the weight of 1 paper clip? Show your work.

_____ $\div$ _____ $=$ _____

Solve the problem. Then read why each answer choice is correct or not correct.

Solve

A penny has a mass of 2.5 grams.

What is the mass of 100 pennies?

2.5 grams

Ⓐ   2,500 grams

Ⓑ   250 grams

Ⓒ   25 grams

Ⓓ   0.025 grams

Check

Check whether you chose the correct answer.

Find $2.5 \times 100 =$ ▨.

To multiply 2.5 by 100, move the decimal point 2 places to the right. Fill in the space with a zero to show the ones place.

$2.5 \times 100 = 250$

So, the correct answer is Ⓑ.

Why are the other answer choices not correct?

Ⓐ 2,500 grams	This is the result of multiplying 2.5 by 1,000. The decimal point was moved to the right 3 places instead of 2 places.
Ⓒ 25 grams	This is the result of multiplying 2.5 by 10. The decimal point was only moved 1 place to the right instead of 2 places.
Ⓓ 0.025 grams	This is the result of dividing 2.5 by 100. The decimal point was moved to the left instead of to the right.

- Identify the operation.
- Write the equation.
- Consider the power of ten.
- Move the decimal point to the right to multiply and to the left to divide.

3. The art teacher ordered 100 sketchbooks for $125. What is the cost for each sketchbook?

Ⓐ $12,500

Ⓑ $12.50

Ⓒ $1.25

Ⓓ $0.125

4. A stamp has a length of 2.54 centimeters.

2.54 cm

Erick drew a picture of the stamp. His picture is 10 times as long as the actual stamp. What is the length of Erick's picture?

Ⓐ 254 cm

Ⓑ 25.4 cm

Ⓒ 0.254 cm

Ⓓ 0.0254 cm

5. Each morning, Mrs. Unger walks 1.75 miles around her neighborhood. What equation can be used to find the number of miles she will have walked in 100 days?

Ⓐ $1.75 \times 10 = $ ▨

Ⓑ $1.75 \times 100 = $ ▨

Ⓒ $1.75 \div 10 = $ ▨

Ⓓ $1.75 \div 100 = $ ▨

6. In which equation does ▨ = 0.49?

Ⓐ $490 \div 100 - $ ▨

Ⓑ $4.9 \times 100 = $ ▨

Ⓒ $49.0 \div 100 = $ ▨

Ⓓ $0.049 \times 1,000 = $ ▨

Study the model. It is a good example of a written answer.

Student Model

Show

Tyler has a box of paper clips. He links together 100 paper clips to make a chain. The chain is 320 centimeters long. How long does each paper clip measure?

Show each step. Then explain how you found the solution.

Divide to find the length of each paper clip.

$320 \div 100 = ?$
$320 \rightarrow 3.20$

Multiply to check.
$3.2 \times 100 = 320$

Solution: _____3.2 cm_____

☑ The student shows each step.

☑ The student correctly answers the question asked.

Explain

Explanation:

Each paper clip is the same length. Tyler uses 100 paper clips. I can divide to find the answer. 100 is a power of ten. To divide a decimal by a power of ten, I move the decimal point to the left. The number of places I move the decimal point is equal to the number of zeros in the power of ten. 100 has two zeros, so I move the decimal point 2 places to the left: $320 \div 100 = 3.20$. I checked my answer by multiplying 3.2 by 100. The product is 320, which matches the length of the chain.

☑ The student gives important details about how to find the length of the paper clip.

☑ The student uses the math words *power of ten*, *multiply*, *divide*, and *decimal point*.

7. A store collected old cell phones to be recycled. If each cell phone weighed 4.76 ounces and they collected 1,000 cell phones, what was the total weight of the phones collected?

   Show each step. Then explain how you found the solution.

✓ CHECKLIST
Did you . . .
☐ show each step?
☐ answer the question asked?
☐ give important details?
☐ use math words?

Solution: _____

Explanation:

_____

_____

_____

_____

_____

As you multiply and divide by powers of ten, you may want to
- write the equation before solving it.
- draw an arrow to show which way to move the decimal point.
- underline the zeros in the power of ten to show how many places to move the decimal point.
- use the inverse operation to check your work.

Solve each problem.

8. Amy ordered 100 bottles of water for the soccer team. Each bottle holds 0.5 liters of water. What is the total liters of water Amy ordered?

   Ⓐ 500 liters

   Ⓑ 50 liters

   Ⓒ 5 liters

   Ⓓ 0.005 liters

9. Which expression has a value of 7.5?

   Ⓐ 0.75 × 100

   Ⓑ 0.75 × 1,000

   Ⓒ 0.075 × 100

   Ⓓ 0.075 × 1,000

10. Under a microscope, an object looks like it is 1.75 inches long. The microscope magnifies the object 10 times. What equation can be used to find the actual length of the object?

    Ⓐ 1.75 ÷ 100 = ▢

    Ⓑ 1.75 × 100 = ▢

    Ⓒ 1.75 ÷ 10 = ▢

    Ⓓ 1.75 × 10 = ▢

11. What is the quotient?

    263.81 ÷ 1,000

    Ⓐ 263,810

    Ⓑ 2,638.1

    Ⓒ 26.381

    Ⓓ 0.26381

12. An architect made a scale model of a building. The height of the model is 13.45 inches. The actual building is 100 times taller. What is the height of the building?

Ⓐ 0.1345 inches

Ⓑ 134.5 inches

Ⓒ 1,345 inches

Ⓓ 13,450 inches

13. Reggie bought a pack of paper at the office supply store for $13.58. There were 1,000 sheets of paper in the pack. What is the cost per sheet of paper?

Ⓐ $135.80

Ⓑ $1.358

Ⓒ $0.1358

Ⓓ $0.01358

14. A stamp measures 2.2 centimeters wide.

2.2 cm

How long is a roll of 100 stamps?

Write and solve an equation to show the total.

_____

_____

15. Mr. Suarez is building a brick patio. He orders 100 red bricks. The cost to deliver the bricks depends on the total weight. Each brick weighs 2.7 kilograms. What is the total weight of Mr. Suarez's order?

Show each step. Then explain how you found the solution.

Solution: _____

Explanation:

_____

_____

_____

_____

Lesson 21 MULTIPLY DECIMALS

PART ONE: Learn About Estimating Products of Decimal Numbers

 **How can you find estimated products of decimal numbers?**

Explore

You can use **multiplication** to find the total of equal groups. This total is the **product**. Some multiplication problems ask for an exact answer. Others ask for an **estimate**, an answer that is close to the exact answer.

The youth baseball league is ordering 19 new uniforms. Each uniform costs $57.30. About how much will the uniforms cost altogether?

$57.30

Think

How many uniforms? __19__

How much is each uniform? __$57.30__

The problem asks, "*About* how much will the uniforms cost?"

Is an exact answer or an estimate needed? __estimate__

Find the estimated product of __$57.30__ and __19__.

Connect

Use rounding to find an estimate. Follow the steps.

Step 1: Round any **decimal numbers** to the nearest whole number.	$57.30 → $57 19 is a whole number.
Step 2: Round numbers to the nearest ten if this will make it easier to multiply.	19 → 20 $57 → $60
Step 3: Multiply the rounded numbers.	20 × $60 = $1,200

The estimate for the cost of the uniforms is $1,200.

Let's Talk

How can you tell if an estimate is greater than or less than the exact answer?

Think It Through

Fill in the blanks as you solve the problem.

A group of 48 people are planning a trip to see a baseball game.
They can order the tickets online. Each ticket costs $27.50.

About how much will it cost to order all the tickets online?

■ How many tickets? _____

How much is each ticket? _____

■ Is an exact answer or an estimate needed? _____

Find the estimated product of _____ and _____.

■ You can use rounding to find an estimate.

Round any decimal numbers to the nearest whole number.

$27.50 → _____   48 is a _____ number.

Round to the nearest ten if this will make it easier to multiply.

$28 → _____   48 → _____

■ Multiply the rounded numbers.

_____ × _____ = _____

Solution: It will cost about _____ to order all the tickets.

> If both factors are rounded to greater numbers, the estimated product will be greater than the actual product. This an **overestimate**.
>
> If both factors are rounded to lesser numbers, the estimated product will be less than the actual product. This Is an **underestimate**.

 Your Turn   **Now, use what you know to solve this problem.**

1. Dylan's father bought 72.8 pounds of steak for a family barbeque. Each pound cost $5.10. About how much did all the steak cost? Show the steps to estimate the product.

72.8 → _____   5.10 → _____

73 → _____

_____ × _____ = _____

All the steak cost about _____.

 **How can you find exact products of decimal numbers?**

Explore

An estimate can help you predict an answer, or check to see if an answer is reasonable. Estimate 2.3 × 0.57.

$$2.3 \rightarrow 2 \text{ and } 0.57 \rightarrow 1$$

$$2 \times 1 = 2$$

So, 2.3 × 0.57 ≈ 2.

How can you find the exact product?

Think

Multiply 2.3 × 0.57.

The first **factor** 2.3 is __2__ ones and __3__ tenths, or __23__ tenths.

The second factor 0.57 is __5__ tenths, __7__ hundredths.

Multiply the first factor by the second factor.

Connect

Organize the problem like you would with whole numbers. Then multiply.

$$\overset{\overset{1}{2}}{2.3} \quad \text{Place the second factor below the first factor.}$$

$$\underline{\times\ 0.57}$$

161   Multiply 7 hundredths × 23 tenths. Record the partial product.

+ 1150   Multiply 5 tenths × 23 tenths. Record the partial product. Use a zero as a placeholder.

1311   Add the two partial products. Write the sum.

Use reasoning to place the **decimal point**. Which makes the most sense: 0.1331, 1.311, 13.11, or 131.1? Since the estimate of 2.3 × 0.57 is about 2, 1.311 makes the most sense. So 2.3 × 0.57 = 1.311.

Let's Talk

How does the exact answer compare to the estimate? Is the estimate an overestimate or an underestimate? Explain.

Think It Through

Fill in the blanks as you solve the problem.

Ms. Berkley stopped for gas. She filled her car's tank with 9.6 gallons of gas. Each gallon cost $2.85. How much did Ms. Berkley spend on gas?

■ First estimate 9.6 × $2.85 → _____ × _____ = _____

■ Then multiply 9.6 × $2.85.

The first factor 9.6 is _____ ones and _____ tenths, or _____ tenths.

The second factor $2.85 is _____ ones and _____ tenths, _____ hundredths.

Multiply the first factor by the second factor.

■ Organize the problem and then multiply.

```
        9.6
   × [_____]
     [_____]     Multiply 5 hundredths × 96 tenths.
     [_____]     Multiply 8 tenths × 96 tenths.
   + [_____]     Multiply 2 ones × 96 tenths.
     [_____]     Add the partial products.
```

■ Use reasoning to place the decimal point.

Since 9.6 × $2.85 is about $30, _____ makes the most sense.

9.6 × $2.85 = _____

Solution: Ms. Berkley spent _____ on gas.

> The number of decimal places in the product is equal to the sum of the decimal places in the factors.
>
> 3.25   2 decimal places
> × 2.1   1 decimal place
> 6.825   3 decimal places

Your Turn ▷ **Now, use what you know to solve this problem.**

2. Apples are on sale for $1.68 a pound. What is the cost of a 4.5-pound bag of apples? Show your work.

_____ × _____ = _____

A 4.5-pound bag of apples costs _____.

Solve the problem. Then read why each answer choice is correct or not correct.

Solve

Jordan is buying fruit to make a fruit salad.
Watermelon is on sale for $0.34 per pound.
He picks a watermelon that weighs 18.4 pounds.

What is the cost of the watermelon?

Ⓐ $6.26 Ⓒ $18.74

Ⓑ $9.00 Ⓓ 62.56

Check

Check whether you chose the correct answer.

Notice that 0.34 is a decimal less than 1. If the decimal is less than 0.5, round to 0.5. If it is greater than 0.5, round to 1.

First, estimate: $0.34 \rightarrow 0.5$, and $18.4 \rightarrow 18$

$0.5 \times 18 = 9$ The actual cost should be close to $9.

Then multiply:

$18.4 \times \$0.34$

$$
\begin{array}{r}
18.4 \\
\times 0.34 \\
\hline
736 \\
+5520 \\
\hline
6.256
\end{array}
$$

> If you round 0.34 to the nearest whole number, you would round it to 0, which would lead to a cost of $0.

Use reasoning to place the decimal point. Round to the nearest penny.

So, the correct answer is Ⓐ.

Why are the other answer choices not correct?

Ⓑ $9.00	This is the estimated product. The problem requires an exact answer.
Ⓒ $18.74	This is the sum of 18.4 and 0.34. The product should be found.
Ⓓ $62.56	The decimal point is placed incorrectly. It should be placed between the digits 6 and 2.

Your Turn ⟩ Solve each problem. Use the hints to avoid mistakes.

- Identify if an estimate or exact answer is needed.
- Organize the problem and multiply as you would whole numbers.
- Use reasoning to place the decimal point in the product.

3. Armand bought bottles of water to give out to the athletes at the track meet. Each bottle had 33.8 fluid ounces of water. The athletes drank 52 bottles of water. How much water did the athletes drink altogether?

  Ⓐ 85.8 fl oz

  Ⓑ 175.76 fl oz

  Ⓒ 1,500 fl oz

  Ⓓ 1,757.6 fl oz

4. Mandy enjoys running. She records the number of miles she runs each week. She runs an average of 15.8 miles each week. About how many miles will she run in a year? (1 year ≈ 52 weeks)

  Ⓐ 821.6 miles

  Ⓑ 800 miles

  Ⓒ 82.16 miles

  Ⓓ 16 miles

5. An animal-shaped eraser costs $0.85. What is the approximate cost of 4 erasers?

  Ⓐ $400.00

  Ⓑ $34.00

  Ⓒ $4.00

  Ⓓ $3.40

6. Which has a product of 17.28?

  Ⓐ 3.2 × 5.4

  Ⓑ 32 × 5.4

  Ⓒ 3.2 × 54

  Ⓓ 3.20 × 0.54

Study the model. It is a good example of a written answer.

Student Model

Show

Arnold is building a brick patio. He is using red pavers. He orders 648 pavers. Each paver costs $0.55. What is the total cost for the pavers?

Show each step. Then explain how you found the solution.

First, estimate the product.

648 → 650   0.55 → 1

650 × 1 = 650

The decimal is greater than 0.5, so round to 1.

Then find the exact product.

```
   648
 ×0.55
  3240
+32400
 356.40
```

Solution: The total cost is $356.40.

> ☑ The student shows each step.

> ☑ The student correctly answers the question asked.

Explain

Explanation:

I need to find the product of 648 × $0.55. I first estimated the product by rounding each factor. I rounded 648 to 650 and 0.55 to 1, and then found 650 × 1 = 650. Then, I found the exact answer by multiplying as I would whole numbers. I used the estimate to place the decimal point. So, 648 × $0.55 = $356.40.

> ☑ The student gives important details about how to find the total cost.

> ☑ The student uses the math words *product*, *estimate*, *factor*, *multiply*, and *decimal point*.

7. Erica is hosting a picnic to celebrate the Fourth of July. She buys 28 large balloons to decorate for the picnic. Each balloon costs $3.45. How much does Erica spend on the balloons?

Show each step. Then explain how you found the solution.

CHECKLIST

Did you . . .

☐ show each step?

☐ answer the question asked?

☐ give important details?

☐ use math words?

Solution: _____

Explanation:

_____

_____

_____

_____

_____

As you solve multiplication problems involving decimals, remember to

- first decide if an estimate or exact answer is needed.
- organize the problem and then multiply.
- use reasoning to place the decimal point.

Solve each problem.

8. Mr. Gregor is replacing the floor in his kitchen. He buys 4 boxes of floor tiles. Each box costs $34.95. How much do the tiles cost altogether?

Ⓐ $126.60

Ⓑ $139.80

Ⓒ $160.00

Ⓓ $1,398.00

9. Which two numbers have an estimated product of 80?

Ⓐ 24 and 39.4

Ⓑ 78.6 and 9.4

Ⓒ 4.1 and 2.3

Ⓓ 3.87 and 21

10. Hannah enjoys knitting. She knitted 9 scarves that were each 6.8 inches wide. She then knitted the scarves together to make a blanket.

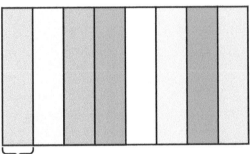

6.8 in.

How long was the blanket?

Ⓐ 612 inches

Ⓑ 61.2 inches

Ⓒ 70 inches

Ⓓ 700 inches

11. Omar bought 2.7 pounds of cashews. Each pound costs $4.90. How much did he spend on cashews?

Ⓐ $0.13

Ⓑ $1.32

Ⓒ $13.23

Ⓓ $132.30

12. A fruit stand sells peaches for $1.65 a pound. Carter buys 2.4 pounds of peaches. About how much did Carter spend on peaches?

Ⓐ $3.96

Ⓑ $39.60

Ⓒ $4.00

Ⓓ $40.00

13. What is the estimated product of 5.6 × 0.37?

Ⓐ 2.072

Ⓑ 3

Ⓒ 6

Ⓓ 20.72

14. Amarion downloads 32 songs and places them in the music folder on his computer. If each song file is 5.81 MB, how much space does Amarion need for the songs he downloads?

Estimate the product. Then find the exact answer.

Estimate:

_____

Exact Answer:

_____

15. Loretta took 76 pictures with her new digital camera. The average file size of a picture is 3.8 MB. She transfers the pictures to her computer. How much space will the pictures take up?

Show each step. Then explain how you found the solution.

Solution: _____

Explanation:

_____

_____

_____

Lesson 22 DIVIDE DECIMALS BY WHOLE NUMBERS

PART ONE: Learn About Estimating Quotients of Decimals and Whole Numbers

How can you estimate the quotient of a decimal and a whole number?

Explore

You can use **estimation** to predict a **quotient** of two **whole numbers** or check that the quotient is reasonable.

55 ÷ 15 = ?

> 55 is close to 60, and
> 60 ÷ 15 = 4.

How can you estimate the quotient of a **decimal** and a whole number?

Think

Estimate 1.86 ÷ 5.
Consider the value of 1.86.

The flat represents 1 __one__.

The rods represent 8 __tenths__.

The cubes represent 6 __hundredths__.

Round 1.86 to the nearest whole number. Is 1.86 closer to 1 or 2? __2__

Connect

Estimate by 1.86 ÷ 5 by finding 2 ÷ 5.

Think of the whole-number dividend as tenths.

2 wholes = 20 tenths

20 tenths ÷ 5 groups = 4 tenths in each group
4 tenths = 0.4
So, 1.86 ÷ 5 ≈ 0.4.

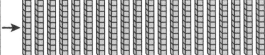

This symbol means "approximately."

Let's Talk

How did using place value help you to estimate the quotient?

Fill in the blanks as you solve the problem.

Six friends have a few bills and coins left over from their trip
to an amusement park. The bills and coins totaled $3.17.

About how much will each friend get if they share the amount equally?

■ Estimate 3.17 ÷ 6.

The dollars represent 3 _____, or _____ hundredths.

The dime represents 1 _____, or _____ hundredths.

The pennies represent 7 _____.

Is 3.17 closer to 3 or 4? _____

■ Estimate by finding 3 ÷ 6.

Think of 3 as _____ hundredths.

_____ hundredths ÷ 6 groups = _____ hundredths

50 hundredths = _____

So, 3.17 ÷ 6 ≈ _____.

Solution: Each friend will get about $ _____.

> Because this problem deals with money, it makes sense to think of the amount in terms of hundredths instead of tenths. 1 penny is 1-hundredth of a dollar.

Your Turn   **Now, use what you know to solve this problem.**

1. Use place value to estimate the quotient of 5.82 ÷ 12.

5.82 ÷ 12 ≈ _____

How can you find an exact quotient of a decimal number and a whole number?

Explore

To divide whole numbers, you can use place value and long division.

How can you divide a decimal by a whole number?

What is 87.45 ÷ 11?

675 ÷ 12

$$
\begin{array}{r}
56\ \text{R}\ 3 \\
12\overline{)675} \\
-60 \\
\hline
75 \\
-72 \\
\hline
3
\end{array}
$$

divisor   quotient   dividend

Think

Estimate first using **compatible numbers**.

87.45 is close to __88__. Divide. __88__ ÷ 11 = __8__

The quotient should be close to __8__.

Then find the exact quotient.

Divide __87.45__ into __11__ equal groups.

Set up the problem. 11)87.45

Connect

Use long division. Follow the steps to divide 87.45 by 11.

$$
\begin{array}{r}
7.95 \\
11\overline{)87.45} \\
-77 \\
\hline
104 \\
-99 \\
\hline
55 \\
-55 \\
\hline
0
\end{array}
$$

There are 7 elevens in 87. Write 7 in the quotient. Multiply 7 × 11 = 77.
Write 77 under 87. Subtract. Bring down the 4 tenths.
There are 9 elevens in 104. Write 9 in the quotient. Multiply 9 × 11 = 99.
Write 99 under 104. Subtract. Bring down the 5 hundredths.
There are 5 elevens in 55. Write 5 in the quotient. Multiply 5 × 11 = 55.
Write 55 under 55. Subtract. The difference is 0.

Place the decimal point in the quotient above the decimal point in the dividend.

So, 87.45 ÷ 11 = 7.95.

Check: The answer of 7.95 is close to the estimate of 8.

Let's Talk

Why is 79.5 an unreasonable quotient for the problem above?

Fill in the blanks as you solve the problem.

Martin spent $48.65 on books. He bought 7 books.
Each book cost the same amount. How much did each book cost?

■ Find: 48.65 ÷ 7 = ?

Estimate first. 48.65 is close to ____. 7 divides evenly into ____.

Divide: ____ ÷ ____ = ____. The quotient should be close to ____.

■ How much in all? _____   How many groups? ____

Divide _____ into ____ equal groups.

Set up the problem. ☐)‾‾‾‾‾

■ Use long division to find the quotient.

Divide, multiply, subtract, bring down, and repeat.

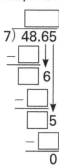

Place the decimal point in the quotient above the decimal point in the dividend.

■ $48.65 ÷ 7 = _____

Solution: Each book cost $_____.

> You can use multiplication to check your answer. Multiply the quotient by the divisor. The product should equal the dividend.
>
> dividend ÷ divisor = quotient
>
> *Check:*
>
> quotient × divisor = dividend

 **Now, use what you know to solve this problem.**

2. Use long division to find the quotient of 54.32 ÷ 4.

54.32 ÷ 4 = _____

Number and Operations   Divide Decimals by Whole Numbers **219**

Solve the problem. Then read why each answer choice is correct or not correct.

Solve

Carlos has 3 boxes to mail to his cousin. He has the boxes weighed at the post office. The total weight is 14.34 pounds.

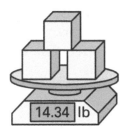

14.34 lb

What is the average weight of each box?

Ⓐ 0.478 lb

Ⓑ 4.11 lb

Ⓒ 4.78 lb

Ⓓ 5.00 lb

The *average* weight of the boxes can be found by dividing the total weight by the number of boxes.

Check

Check whether you chose the correct answer.

Estimate first. 15 ÷ 3 = 15
Divide to find the average weight.

14.34 ÷ 3 = 4.78

This is close to the estimate of 5.

So, the correct answer is Ⓒ.

Why are the other answer choices not correct?

```
        4.78
    3)14.34
     -12
       23
      -21
        24
       -24
         0
```

Ⓐ 0.478 lb	The decimal point should be between the digits 4 and the 7, not before the 4.	
Ⓑ 4.11 lb	The leftover ones need to be regrouped as tenths, and the leftover tenths as hundredths.	
Ⓓ 5.00 lb	This is an estimated quotient. The question asks for an exact answer.	

Your Turn ⟩ Solve each problem. Use the hints to avoid mistakes.

- Identify if an estimate or an exact answer is needed.
- Use long division to find the quotient.
- Place the decimal point in the quotient above the decimal point in the dividend.

3. The soccer team ordered new uniforms. The total cost of the order was $414.72. The team ordered 12 uniforms. What was the cost per uniform?

Ⓐ $3.46

Ⓑ $31.60

Ⓒ $34.56

Ⓓ $44.56

4. A bag of apples weighs 1.65 pounds. There are 5 apples in the bag. The apples are all about the same size. About how much does one apple weigh?

Ⓐ 0.02 pounds

Ⓑ 0.40 pounds

Ⓒ 2.5 pounds

Ⓓ 10 pounds

5. Keisha began a walking program. She recorded the number of miles she walked each day. At the end of 4 weeks, she had walked a total of 86.8 miles. What was the average number of miles she walked per week?

Ⓐ 2.17 miles

Ⓑ 20 miles

Ⓒ 21.7 miles

Ⓓ 347.2 miles

6. Which has an estimated quotient of 0.8?

Ⓐ $36.12 \div 5 =$ ▨

Ⓑ $4.1 \div 5 =$ ▨

Ⓒ $47.07 \div 5 =$ ▨

Ⓓ $0.43 \div 5 =$ ▨

Study the model. It is a good example of a written answer.

Student Model

Show

Marisa bought tickets to see her favorite singer.

She spent $96.75 on 3 tickets. How much did each ticket cost?

Show each step. Then explain how you found the solution.

Divide.

$$
\begin{array}{r}
32.25 \\
3\overline{)96.75} \\
-9\downarrow \\
\overline{06} \\
-6\downarrow \\
\overline{07} \\
-6\downarrow \\
\overline{15} \\
-15 \\
\overline{0}
\end{array}
$$

Check.

$$
\begin{array}{r}
32.25 \\
\times 3 \\
\hline
96.75
\end{array}
$$

> ☑ The student shows each step.

Solution: __Each ticket cost $32.25.__

> ☑ The student correctly answers the question asked.

Explain

Explanation:

The total is $96.75. There are 3 groups. I divided 96.75

by 3 to find the cost per ticket. I used long division and

placed the decimal point in the quotient above the decimal

point in the dividend. I found that each ticket cost $32.75.

I checked my answer by multiplying the quotient by the

divisor. The product was the dividend, so my answer

is correct.

> ☑ The student gives important details about how to find the cost of each ticket.

> ☑ The student uses the math words *decimal point*, *quotient*, *dividend*, and *divisor*.

7. Tamika and her friends ate lunch at a restaurant. The total cost of the lunch for the 5 of them was $36.15. They divide the bill equally. How much does each friend owe?

Show each step. Then explain how you found the solution.

✓ CHECKLIST
Did you . . .
☐ show each step?
☐ answer the question asked?
☐ give important details?
☐ use math words?

Solution: _____

Explanation:

_____

_____

_____

_____

_____

As you divide decimal numbers, remember to
- estimate the quotient before dividing.
- be sure you placed the decimal point correctly in the quotient.
- use multiplication to check your work.

Solve each problem.

8. A box of 8 pencils costs $3.76.

About how much does one pencil cost?

Ⓐ $0.40

Ⓑ $0.50

Ⓒ $5

Ⓓ $32

9. What number goes in the box to make the equation true?

$$28.89 \div 9 = \boxed{}$$

Ⓐ 3

Ⓑ 3.21

Ⓒ 4.21

Ⓓ 32.1

10. Joe ran a race that was 26.20 miles long. He ran the race in 4 hours. What was the average number of miles Joe ran each hour?

Ⓐ 6 miles

Ⓑ 6.05 miles

Ⓒ 6.55 miles

Ⓓ 7.55 miles

11. A grocery store has a sale on soup.

Soup Sale!

4 cans for $5.00

What is the cost for one can of soup?

Ⓐ $1.25

Ⓑ $0.80

Ⓒ $0.20

Ⓓ $0.13

12. Oscar is making potato salad for a picnic. He buys a 6-pound bag of potatoes for $3.54. What is the cost per pound?

Ⓐ $0.06

Ⓒ $5.90

Ⓑ $0.59

Ⓓ $21.24

13. What is the quotient?

$$63.72 \div 6$$

Ⓐ 1.062

Ⓒ 16.2

Ⓑ 10.62

Ⓓ 106.2

14. Riley just finished knitting a scarf. The scarf is 35.58 inches long. Riley knitted the scarf in 6 days. What is the average length of scarf Riley knit each day?

Estimate the quotient, and then find the exact answer.

Estimate:

_____

Exact Answer:

_____

15. The coach ordered warm-up suits for the gymnasts. The 7 warm-up suits cost a total of $296.59. How much does each gymnast owe?

Show each step. Then explain how you found the solution.

Solution: _____

Explanation:

_____

_____

_____

_____

How can you estimate the quotient of two decimal numbers?

Explore

You can **estimate** the **quotient** of decimals and whole numbers.

To estimate 3.2 ÷ 6, you can round the decimal to the nearest whole number. Round 3.2 to 3.

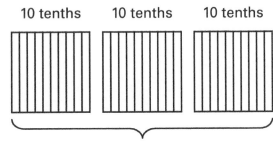

10 tenths   10 tenths   10 tenths

Then find 3 ÷ 6.

> 30 tenths ÷ 6 = 5 tenths
>
> 5 tenths = 0.5

So, 3.2 ÷ 6 ≈ 0.5.

3 = 30 tenths

How can you estimate the quotient of two **decimal numbers**?

Think

Estimate 46.7 ÷ 6.7.

46.7 rounded to the nearest whole number is ___47___.

6.7 rounded to the nearest whole number is ___7___.

Use **compatible numbers** to find the estimated quotient. Find numbers close to the actual numbers that are easy to divide mentally.

What compatible numbers can you use to estimate 47 ÷ 7? Think of a basic division fact you already know.

___49___ ÷ ___7___

Connect

Estimate 46.7 ÷ 6.7 by finding 49 ÷ 7.

49 ÷ 7 = 7

So, 46.7 ÷ 6.7 ≈ 7.

Let's Talk

Why do you need to use the ≈ symbol instead of the = symbol in the math sentence 46.7 ÷ 6.7 ≈ 7?

Fill in the blanks as you solve the problem.

A length of railroad track that is 35.26 feet long needs to be replaced.
A new railroad tie must be placed every 2.85 feet.
About how many railroad ties are needed to repair this length of track?

■ You need to estimate _____ ÷ _____.

    35.26 rounded to the nearest whole number is _____.

    2.85 rounded to the nearest whole number is _____.

■ Use compatible numbers to estimate the quotient.

    What compatible numbers can you use to estimate 35 ÷ 3?

    Think of a basic division fact.

    _____ ÷ _____

■ Estimate 35.26 ÷ 2.85 by finding _____ ÷ _____.

    _____ ÷ _____ = _____

    So, 35.26 ÷ 2.85 ≈ _____.

Solution: About _____ railroad ties are needed to repair the length of track.

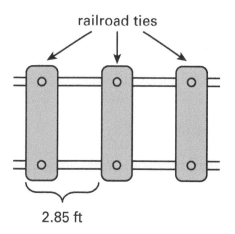

railroad ties

2.85 ft

The symbol ≈ means "approximately equal to." It indicates an estimated answer.

Your Turn

Now, use what you know to solve this problem.

1. There are 55.7 ounces of trail mix in a bin. A factory worker puts 9.3 ounces in each bag. About how many bags can the worker fill?

How can you find an exact quotient of two decimal numbers?

Explore

To divide a decimal number by a whole number, you can use long division. Be sure to place the decimal point correctly in the quotient.

How can you divide a decimal by a decimal?

$$\begin{array}{r} 9.6 \\ 3\overline{)28.8} \\ -27\downarrow \\ \hline 1\,8 \\ -1\,8 \\ \hline 0 \end{array}$$

Think

Find 68.04 ÷ 2.1.

Set up the problem: $2.1\overline{)68.04}$

Divide __68.04__ into __2.1__ equal groups. Find how much is in each group.

It's difficult to divide a number into 2.1 groups. To make this easier, multiply both numbers by a **power of ten** so that the **divisor** is a whole number. Multiply each number by the same power of ten.

2.1 × __10__ = 21, and 68.04 × __10__ = __680.4__.

Rewrite the problem. $21\overline{)680.4}$

Connect

Use long division to find the quotient.

$$\begin{array}{r} 32.4 \\ 21\overline{)680.4} \\ -63\downarrow \\ \hline 50 \\ -42\downarrow \\ \hline 84 \\ -84 \\ \hline 0 \end{array}$$

There are three 21s in 68. Write 3 in the quotient. Multiply 3 × 21 = 63.
Write 63 under 68. Subtract. Bring down the 0 ones.
There are two 21s in 50. Write 2 in the quotient. Multiply 2 × 21 = 42.
Write 42 under 50. Subtract. Bring down the 4 tenths.
There are four 21s in 84. Write 4 in the quotient. Multiply 4 × 21 = 84.
Write 84 under 84. Subtract. The difference is 0.

Place the decimal point in the quotient above the decimal point in the **dividend**.

680.4 ÷ 21 = 32.4, so 68.04 ÷ 2.1 = 32.4.

Let's Talk

You could have multiplied 2.1 and 68.04 by 100 to make both whole numbers. Why is it only necessary to multiply by 10?

Fill in the blanks as you solve the problem.

During a weekend road trip, the Wasserstein family traveled 279.3 miles. They used 9.8 gallons of gasoline. What is the average number of miles they traveled per gallon of gas?

- You need to find how many groups of _____ are in _____.

  Set up the division problem. ⬜)⬜

- To make the divisor a whole number, multiply it by _____.
  9.8 × _____ = _____

  Multiply the dividend by the same power of ten.
  279.3 × _____ = _____

  Rewrite the problem. ⬜)⬜

- Use long division to find the quotient.

  There is an understood decimal point at the end of the whole-number dividend.

  Bring the decimal point up into the quotient.

  Divide, multiply, subtract, bring down, and repeat.

  Because there is a remainder, write a 0 after the decimal and keep dividing.

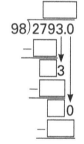

Look at the number of decimal places in the divisor to determine which power of ten to multiply by.

Solution: The Wassersteins traveled an average of _____ miles per gallon.

Your Turn ▷ **Now, use what you know to solve this problem.**

2. What is the exact quotient? Show your work.
   3.41 ÷ 1.55

3.41 ÷ 1.55 = _____

Solve the problem. Then read why each answer choice is correct or not correct.

Solve

What is the quotient of 3.9 ÷ 0.78?

Ⓐ 0.2

Ⓑ 0.5

Ⓒ 2

Ⓓ 5

Check

Check whether you chose the correct answer.

Set up the long-division problem. $0.78\overline{)3.9}$

Rewrite the division problem with a whole-number divisor.

$$0.78 \times 100 = 78 \qquad 3.9 \times 100 = 390$$

$$78\overline{)390}$$

Use long division to find the quotient.

$$\begin{array}{r} 5 \\ 78\overline{)390} \\ -390 \\ \hline 0 \end{array}$$

So, the correct answer is Ⓓ.

Why are the other answer choices not correct?

Ⓐ 0.2	The dividend and divisor were switched; 78 was divided by 390. Divide 390 by 78.
Ⓑ 0.5	The divisor was multiplied by 100, but the dividend was only multiplied by 10. The dividend and the divisor must be multiplied by the same power of ten.
Ⓒ 2	The dividend and divisor were switched. The divisor was multiplied by 100, but the dividend was only multiplied by 10.

- Use compatible numbers to estimate a quotient.

- Set up a division problem correctly. $\text{divisor}\overline{)\text{dividend}}^{\text{quotient}}$

- Multiply both divisor and dividend by the same power of ten so that the divisor becomes a whole number.

- Continue the long-division process until there is no remainder, writing in zeros as needed.

3. A box contains 6.2 ounces of seasoned rice. One serving size is 1.9 ounces. About how many servings of rice are in the box?

   Ⓐ   3

   Ⓑ   4

   Ⓒ   6

   Ⓓ   12

4. Which division problem is best to use for estimating the quotient of 51.3 ÷ 11.9?

   Ⓐ $55\overline{)11}$

   Ⓑ $11\overline{)55}$

   Ⓒ $48\overline{)12}$

   Ⓓ $12\overline{)48}$

5. What number will make the equation true?

   $$48.45 \div 0.95 = \rule{1cm}{0.4pt}$$

   Ⓐ   0.02

   Ⓑ   0.51

   Ⓒ   2

   Ⓓ   51

6. Ming paid $1.05 for 2.5 pounds of bananas. What was the cost per pound?

   Ⓐ $0.24

   Ⓑ $0.42

   Ⓒ $2.38

   Ⓓ $4.20

Study the model. It is a good example of a written answer.

Student Model

Show

A hummingbird beat its wings 150.5 times in 2.15 seconds. How many times did it beat its wings each second?

Show your work. Check that your answer is reasonable using estimation. Then explain how you found the solution.

Write the division problem. $2.15\overline{)150.5}$

Multiply by a power of ten.
$2.15 \times 100 = 215$
$150.5 \times 100 = 15,050$

$$\begin{array}{r} 70 \\ 215\overline{)15050} \\ -\underline{1505}\!\downarrow \\ 00 \\ -\underline{0} \\ 0 \end{array}$$

☑ The student shows each step.

Estimate to check. $2\overline{)150}$ $\quad 75\;\checkmark$

Solution: The hummingbird beat its wings 70 times each second.

☑ The student correctly answers the question asked.

Explain

Explanation:

First, I set up the long-division problem. Then, I multiplied

the divisor and dividend by 100 to make the divisor a whole

number. I wrote the new division problem and followed the

steps to divide. The quotient is 70. I checked my answer

using estimation. I estimated the quotient of 150.5 ÷ 2.15

using compatible numbers: 150 ÷ 2 = 75. So, my answer

of 70 beats each second is reasonable because it is close to

the estimate.

☑ The student gives important details about how to find the quotient.

☑ The student uses the math words *divisor, dividend, quotient, estimation,* and *compatible numbers.*

7. Jasmine's mother paid $21.60 for 3.2 pounds of sliced ham for a party. What was the price per pound?

Show your work. Check that your answer is reasonable using estimation. Then explain how you found the solution.

> **CHECKLIST**
>
> Did you . . .
>
> ☐ show all your work?
>
> ☐ answer the question asked?
>
> ☐ give important details?
>
> ☐ use math words?

Solution: _____

Explanation:

_____

_____

_____

_____

_____

_____

As you divide decimals, remember to
• multiply both parts by the same power of ten to make the divisor a whole number.
• use compatible numbers to estimate the answer to check for reasonableness.

Solve each problem.

8. Which is the best pair of compatible numbers for estimating the quotient of 31.2 ÷ 4.9?

Ⓐ 28 and 4
Ⓑ 30 and 5
Ⓒ 31 and 5
Ⓓ 32 and 4

9. Alejandro planted a tree for Earth Day. It grew 25.4 inches in 6.3 months. About how much did the tree grow each month during those 6 months?

Ⓐ about 4 inches
Ⓑ about 5 inches
Ⓒ about 150 inches
Ⓓ about 180 inches

10. Marnie wants to multiply 9.6 and 0.42 by a power of ten so that she will have a whole-number divisor. What number should she multiply by?

9.6 ÷ 0.42

Ⓐ 1
Ⓑ 10
Ⓒ 100
Ⓓ 1,000

11. Marlena bought a bottle containing 3.5 milliliters of face soap. She uses 0.05 milliliter of the soap every day. How many days will the soap last before she needs to buy a new bottle?

Ⓐ 7
Ⓑ 14
Ⓒ 70
Ⓓ 175

12. How many groups of 0.3 are in 0.048?

Ⓐ 0.0625
Ⓑ 0.016
Ⓒ 0.16
Ⓓ 6.25

13. What is 84 hundredths divided by 24 hundredths?

Ⓐ 0.035
Ⓑ 3.5
Ⓒ 4
Ⓓ 5

14. Estimate the quotient. Explain how you got your answer.

$$77.5 \div 10.2 \approx \boxed{}$$

_____

_____

_____

15. Layla and her mother are sewing costumes for the school play. They purchased 6.8 yards of fabric for $67.66. What was the price for each yard of fabric?

Show your work. Check the reasonableness of your answer using estimation.

Then explain how you found the solution.

Solution: _____

Explanation:

_____

_____

_____

_____

_____